ROCHESTRIVIA

By

Pete Dobrovitz

An illuminating look at Rochester

Big Kids Publishing, Inc.
Rochester, New York

First Print July, 1984
5,000 copies

For more information and orders:

Big Kids Publishing, Inc.
P.O. Box 10237
Rochester, New York 14610

ISBN 0-930249-00-3

ROCHESTRIVIA
Acknowledgements

VERONICA SLIVINSKI
Editor

HILARIE HUGHES
Artist

PETE DOBROVITZ
Photographer

PAT DOBROVITZ
Sales/Promotion

Special thanks:

- Sally "Fan Fare" Stookey, our publishing mentor
- Len Lustik, who provided much needed pessimism and accounting assistance
- Tom Fitzpatrick, the lawyer who made the dream of two "big kids" a corporation

No acknowledgements would be complete without a deep bow to the great historians and journalists who've done such a thorough job chronicling the history of this wonderful city, especially Blake McKelvey, Shirley Cox Husted, George Beahon, Joseph Barnes, Matt Jackson, Henry Clune, Maude West, Howard Hosmer, Eleanor Kalsbeck and Arch Merrill.

Finally, my gratitude to the staff of the Rundel Library's Local History Department, for patiently replacing all the clip files that they allowed me to rummage through! And to all of you, who so graciously answered my off-the-wall questions with no idea why I wanted the information!

This book is dedicated to
the two beautiful ladies of my life—
Patti, my wife
and
Sarah, our daughter

ABOUT THE AUTHOR

PETER EDWARD DOBROVITZ

Born: 3/6/53 Strong Memorial *Nationality:* Rochesterian

Education:

School #49, Lattimore Road
St. Anne's, Mount Hope Avenue
Brookview, Brookview Drive
St. Margaret Mary, Rogers Parkway
Bishop Kearney High, Kings Highway
Marquette University, Milwaukee . . . Milwaukee?

Careers (1968-present):

Bagboy, Wegmans Supermarket
Men's clothing sales, Sibley's
Quality control, Eastman Kodak
Reporter, WROC-TV
Reporter/producer, WOKR-TV

Favorite foods:

Al's Stand lemon ice, Zweigle's white hots, Smittey's ribs, Meisenzahl chocolate chip ice cream, Pic 'n' Pay 1¢ candy, Casa Larga Riesling, Genny Cream Ale, Red Creek artichokes.

Favorite pastimes:

Willow Point Park amusement cars, the Corn Hill Festival, watching Gerry Cheevers and Dave Vineyard, listening to the Brass Buttons and the original Duke Jupiter—live.

Photo: David Parrotta Backroom Productions

TABLE OF CONTENTS

ABOUT THE BOOK

Roch•es•triv•ia /räch-es-triv-e-uh/ *n* 1: a fun book to be read and enjoyed 2: a game to be played (six color-coded sections are helpful in the **pursuit of trivia**) 3: facts that are funny, thought-provoking, informative and entertaining (hopefully all at the same time!)

Dear Reader,

It may be easier to tell you what ROCHESTRIVIA is not. It is not a textbook or a master's thesis. There are no profound conclusions or grand overview.

ROCHESTRIVIA is a mosaic: 1,834 little tiles, each with a little tale to tell of the city born in 1834. It's only when you step back from the book that some patterns may begin to emerge if you look hard enough.

You'll see a city with a rich heritage of entertainers: some of modern culture's true giants and some pretty fascinating "might have beens." Our history is dotted with great achievements as well as moments when we were less than we were capable of being. The Great Glacier rolled away to unveil a river valley brimming with beautiful sights and some quirks of creation. Only God can make the Upper Falls, but it took man to make the Can of Worms! Our forefathers worked hard for their money, too! Sometimes the "work ethic" was spurred on by silly ambitions. And we've never been at a loss for the thrills of a Calder Cup or the agony of an Oriole call-up!

Unless otherwise noted, all the questions in this book pertain to people and events **within** Monroe County. Questions concerning the current population are based on the latest government census.

ROCHESTRIVIA is a gift to all who thrive on "lake effect snow," who've mastered alternate street parking and who (through fate or choice) decided they would rather be in Rochester! If some questions seem obvious—congratulations, you're a Rochesterian! If you're a native but are stumped by some of this, don't worry. That's the enlightening part. Remember the words of Woody Allen: "The brain is a highly overrated organ!" Just sit back, relax and enjoy it!

ENTERTAINMENT

1. To Rochesterians she was Lucille Oshinski. But she was Lucille Barkley to Bop Hope in *The Road To Rio*; and to Ronald Reagan, her co-star in a cult classic. Name it.

2. What was the name of Chuck Mangione's first recorded concert with the Rochester Philharmonic Orchestra?

3. A triple bill of *Uriah Heep*, *ZZ Top*, and *Earth, Wind & Fire* was the first concert ever staged at this facility in 1973.

4. In 1983, U of R professor Paul Cherkasky unveiled a new weight reduction plan that featured the "unit concept" of calorie counting. What was the title of his book?

5. He played with the Rochester Royals before starring as TV's Lucas McCain in *The Rifleman*.

6. Formed with a core of Brockport State students, this dance troupe was named for its lack of pro experience, *but* great potential.

7. This religious practice was a daily staple of WSAY radio programming for years.

8. Rochesterians know him for news, but this winner of the Bronze Star and Purple Heart came to town in 1954 to do Red Wing play-by-play on WBBF.

9. It was Rochester's first televised quiz show.

10. At the turn of the century, one Rochester physician blamed this for the sudden increase in pregnancies in women, ages 18 to 20.

ENTERTAINMENT

11. PACE stands for what summertime festival?

12. The only Rochester rock group to ever appear on *The Ed Sullivan Show,* it was the back-up band for Liza Minelli.

13. This new form of entertainment debuted in Rochester at the Baptist Temple in 1927.

14. From his Cypress Street home he moved to Chicago to study law. He ended up with a career that he began by singing "Hi De Hi" in nightclubs.

15. One of the first hour-long morning shows on WOKR was called simply, *Louise.* What was Louise's last name?

16. This jazz club derived its name from the building's former owners, the Knights of Columbus and the Odd Fellows.

17. In the *Saturday Night Fever* era, he was the undisputed king of the disco disc jockeys. His throne was the Winfield Grill, and later, Commodore Vanderbilt's.

18. His long show business career began in Rochester on the stage of the Gaiety Burlesque Theater. The year was 1923 when he was the 3-year-old son of star Joe Yule.

19. In 1951, this sports celebrity hosted a weekly 15-minute program on WHAM-TV that featured grade school kids in boxing matches.

20. This book was reviewed in Rochester's *Daily Advertiser* in 1830. The reviewer wrote, "It is an evidence of fraud, blasphemy and incredulity." What was the book's title?

ENTERTAINMENT

21. In 1980, Rochesterian Thom McKee set a Guinness world record for the most money won on a single game show, $229,000. What was the show?

22. It was the first thing ever broadcast on Rochester radio. It was heard at 11 a.m., March 1, 1922.

23. This Rochester radio station signed on the air on July 9, 1971 by playing Ravel's *Bolero* for 33 continuous hours.

24. Jazzman Fred Costello has played in Rochester nightclubs for years. His biggest crowds, however, hear him in two other "night spots." Name them.

25. While a WOKR-TV weatherman in 1973, he first introduced the "Weather Bird," and later, "The Weather Picture of the Day," drawn by local school children.

26. In 1923, this silent screen star made a public appearance in Rochester. He wowed a standing-room-only audience of women by dancing with his wife on stage.

27. In 1952, a court ruling found these amusement halls all to be illegal. Sheriff Al Skinner moved quickly to shut them all down. What was the amusement?

28. Where does Santa Claus reside inside Midtown Plaza?

29. 9,000 ecstatic fans packed the War Memorial in 1977 to see this "band" whose elaborate stage show featured dancers and sex symbol Tom Netherton.

30. In real life, Joyce Randolph married Rochesterian Dick Charles. But in 1950's TV she starred as a wife named Trixie in a hit series. Name the show and her TV husband.

ENTERTAINMENT

31. Rochester's Soap Box Derby was traditionally held on this hilly thoroughfare.

32. This Rochester group has performed for Princess Grace Kelly of Monaco, Pope Paul VI in Rome, and for the people of Dublin, Ireland, on 8 St. Patrick's Days.

33. He's the only Rochester broadcaster to ever be elected to the city's *Bowling Hall of Fame.*

34. Rochester's labor unions staged this first annual event, locally, in September 1888.

35. In 1958, the Reverend George Ulp, a Presbyterian, began the county's first (and last) drive-in church. Where were Sunday services held?

36. In 1899, "The Jolly Jabbernowls" and "The Rubbernecks" were the first of their kind to be printed in Rochester. What were they?

37. Name the roller coasters at Sea Breeze and at the now-defunct Olympic Park.

38. This Lebanese television star was known as Amus Jacobs when he lived on Nassau Street with his aunt in 1928.

39. What were *Lincoln Zephyr, Typical Blimp,* and *Gunther's Bus*?

40. What was the first channel number on Rochester television?

ENTERTAINMENT

41. On the *Buckeroo Club*, he's Ranger Bob, but at the drop of his 20-gallon hat, he can become "Granny" or "Lenny Goobner," to name only two. What's his true identity?

42. Twentieth Century Fox Studios bought the rights to her story. The working title was "The President's Woman." What Rochesterian wrote it?

43. McQuaid's Father William O'Malley was typecast as a priest in this blockbuster horror film.

44. For years, Jim Boyd has appeared on TV commercials as every Rochesterian's neighbor, but he's really an actor from the Big Apple. What's his character's name?

45. As the head of Columbia Records, this Rochesterian was responsible for the discovery and release of Jimmy Boyd's "I Saw Mommy Kissing Santa Claus."

46. In 1980, Mercy High grad Elaine Bromka decided she'd play an Auschwitz warden instead of an inmate so that she wouldn't have to shave her head. What was the title of the TV film?

47. The husband of opera star Leontyne Price, this former Edison Tech vocal student introduced "Ol' Man River" in the musical, *Showboat*.

48. Following his show at the War Memorial in 1976, he was arrested and charged with possession of a half pound of pot.

49. Chuck Mangione earned an Emmy Award in 1980 for his theme music to the Lake Placid Winter Olympics. What was the song title?

50. This Rochester School Board member became the city's first black television reporter.

ENTERTAINMENT

51. In the fall of 1969, WOKR-TV studios were picketed by viewers upset with the station's decision to discontinue this unusual soap opera.

52. For years, the Eastman House issued awards to honor the old-time stars of silent films. Winners included Mary Pickford, Harold Lloyd, and the Gish sisters. What were these awards called?

53. Twenty-six-year-old Paul Pape of Penfield played "Double J," sidekick of Tony Manero in this 1978 film.

54. On the radio they were "The Old Professor," "Brother Joe," and "Mr. Lee." What were their real names?

55. Shot on the shores of Lake Ontario, this 1981 film features the music of the *Sex Pistols*, *B-52's*, and the acting debut of newsman Dick Burt.

56. Newsman Ken Powell hosted a daily amateur hour for children on the deck of his WROC-TV "Showboat." What was his character name?

57. For years, WVOR's Dan Guilfoyle has hosted a Sunday night program that features oldies, particularly the "Doo-Wop" sound of the 50's. What's the show called?

58. At the turn of the century, this Rochester *necropolis* was a favorite picnic spot because of its rolling terrain and landscaping.

59. Are there more AM or more FM stations on Rochester radio?

60. When he appeared at the Corinthian Theater, the Rochester telephone directory listed him as "William Cody, entertainer."

ENTERTAINMENT

61. It was the original name for the site of The Mason Jar, and later, C.W. West nightclub.

62. Although he had an acute interest in music, George Eastman never played an instrument. He did try, though, buying this instrument on the installment plan as a boy.

63. Playing to a crowd of 16,000 in the late 70's, they were the first major rock band to play in Holleder Stadium.

64. In 1965, the *Hollywood Reporter* heralded this Rochesterian as "The hottest new discovery since Paul Newman. . . ."

65. In 1974, this foreign film star was the pre-game "activity" as she threw in the first ball at the Lancers' home opener.

66. Mayoral candidates Peter Barry and Robert Corris took part in Rochester TV's first one.

67. Rochesterians returning from the Montreal Winter Carnival introduced this winter activity in 1885.

68. Through the 60's, Jerry Carr emerged weekly from his casket in a dungeon to host a program that featured horror films. What was the show called?

69. Edison's kinetoscopes were first displayed locally in the basement of this Rochester department store in 1894.

70. In 1976, with 12 million copies of his live record sold, he packed the War Memorial. Five years later, though, he couldn't fill the 1,000-seat Triangle Theater.

ENTERTAINMENT

71. Drive-ins were the rage in the 50's, but only 4 remained in operation in Monroe County in 1983. Name them.

72. In the summer of 1944, city residents gathered at Cobbs Hill Park for lively free concerts of German music. Who were the singers?

73. This silent screen star attended the Rochester Free Academy in 1905 under her real name, Theodosia Goodman.

74. Eddie Dunn was the first host of this popular radio show which premiered on WHAM in 1960.

75. Harold Smith dropped out of a city high school to pursue a career in professional lacrosse here. It was only after he left Rochester in 1939 that this native American would change his name and become a TV legend. Who was he?

76. In 1971, WOKR decided to broadcast *Mike Douglas* and *Merv Griffin* instead of daily network news coverage of this historic test of constitutional power.

77. In 1979 this group hoped to raise funds for the Special Olympics. The city banned its performance, though, because it would have been "too loud."

78. From what downtown location did Jerry Carr broadcast *The Weather Outside*?

79. In the mid-70's, Rochesterian Brad Edwards played the heavy on 4 out of 5 shows in this series, usually killed in every episode by Steve McGarrett. Name the show.

80. She was Rochester's first anchorwoman on an evening newscast.

ENTERTAINMENT

81. In 1980, Dwight Glodell and James Morley wrote a song. The Chamber of Commerce spent nearly a half million dollars promoting it. Name that tune.

82. He was the "Voice of the Red Wings" for 12 years, longer than any other man.

83. Did the *Beatles* ever perform in Rochester?

84. Called the *Bijou-Dream*, it was Rochester's first, opening in 1906.

85. TV personality Eddie Meath collected money to buy toys for hospitalized children. What was and still is the name of this fund drive?

86. Where did the *Stage* III theater group stage its productions?

87. Before joining WHEC-TV as sports director, Rich Funke was *news* director at a Rochester radio station. Which one?

88. While visiting Rochester in 1958, this star of the *General Electric Theater* said, "I'm no hero. I'm afraid I'm just like the guy next door."

89. It is the city's first public playground and stands in the shadow of the Kodak Office Building.

90. During its local run, PM *Magazine* had 3 successive female co-hosts. Name them.

ENTERTAINMENT

91. In 1937, newsman Al Sigl broadcast a county-wide appeal. Citizens responded with 75 gallons. Of what?

92. These "sports" amusement centers grew so rapidly in the 1930's that the city had to develop codes to regulate them.

93. For years she answered the television question: "What's Cooking?"

94. You can still pedal them in Boston parks; not here any more. But from 1907 to 1927 they were the fashionable way to go on Seneca Park Lake. What were they?

95. What was the name of Bat McGrath and Don Potter's Ridge and Dewey coffeehouse which was named after their cat?

96. Although it overlooks the lake, and not the river, you can bet Sam Patch would have loved this amusement park ride.

97. Hollywood director George Cukor began by directing the Lyceum Theater Stock Company in Rochester. He earned his Oscar directing Rex Harrison in 1964. What was the film?

98. The Rochester Broncos baseball roster once included a player named Reddy Grey. His brother would gain greater fame as author of *Riders of the Purple Sage*. Who was his brother?

99. These 200 Rochester voices join together for 3 performances a year, every year. What are they collectively called?

100. They were the first Rochester-based group to appear in a rock video broadcast on MTV, in 1982.

ENTERTAINMENT

101. In the 30's and 40's young people met at such "singles bars" as The Odenbach, Maggs Ice Cream Parlor, and The Seneca. There was dancing, but no liquor was served. What were these social events called?

102. This nationally known TV songstress gave up her career to marry a funeral parlor director and become a Rochester housewife.

103. In 1942, Ingrid Lindstrom left Rochester for a new job. Of it, she wrote a friend, "I have no idea what it's about." What was the job?

104. In 1906, young boys were hired by a local movie theater to stamp their feet and pound glasses on tables. Why?

105. His TV show was called *Life Is Worth Living.*

106. This Rochester firm won an Oscar in 1954 for production of the cinemascope camera.

107. This star of an early TV western lived his first two years in Rochester; he says all he remembers is snow and women in fur coats.

108. From 1936 to 1950, Rochesterian Wayne Shoemaker scripted radio dramas for WHAM. These dramas were based on actual files of police reports. What was this radio show called?

109. At the Eastman Theatre in 1974, he drove a sellout crowd wild, wearing a mink coat and red hot pants.

110. With what phrase did local sportscaster George Beahon end every sportscast?

ENTERTAINMENT

111. For years, comic Jack Eagle has done "miraculous" things for Xerox products. What has he done?

112. Rochesterians had celebrated V-E and V-J days, but on June 11, 1949, they celebrated an event unrelated to the war. What was June 11, 1949, officially known as in Rochester?

113. This Monroe County beauty contest was finally discontinued in the 1970's, and replaced with the *Youth Cares* awards.

114. This song by the local group the *Invictas* popularized a dance that was considered risque and suggestive then, and probably still would be.

115. His totally tasteless food stamp joke earned him a three-day suspension from his WBBF morning show in 1980.

116. On his weather map, Bob Mills posted scores of his games against Tom Decker. What was the sport?

117. This was the original name of Ranger Bob's *Buckeroo Club* on WUHF-TV.

118. What was Eddie Meath's nickname?

119. He starred as "Grandpa Whiskers" on the *Ann's Attic* TV show for kids.

120. He starred in *MacArthur* and in *To Kill A Mockingbird*, but it was his father who was born here, at the Park Avenue Hospital, on August 3, 1886.

ENTERTAINMENT

121. The city's first one was set up in front of the Grove Street Lutheran Church in 1841 by German nurseryman George Ellwanger, honoring a custom from his ancestors.

122. He made his screen debut with Marlon Brando and Elizabeth Taylor in John Huston's *Reflections In A Golden Eye.*

123. For 25 years they awakened Rochester on WHAM radio.

124. By 1958, 100% of Rochester households had one.

125. In the mid-60's, Brightonian Steve Alaimo was one of the featured singers on this weekly network TV "rock-n-roll show."

126. In their TV commercial, what did singer Don Potter and trumpeter Jeff Tyzik say Rochester had?

127. What do Josh Gardens Florists and Hill TV have in common?

128. In the 1920's, 3,500 Rochesterians were subscribing to this Sunday newspaper, still a popular Sunday indulgence.

129. Because of ownership changes, WROC-TV, Channel 8, has occupied two other number slots on the dial. What were they?

130. He began his TV career on KRLD in Dallas in 1965, two years after Dan Rather left there on the fame of his Kennedy assassination coverage. Rather went to the network; this guy's still trying.

ENTERTAINMENT

131. Unveiled in Seneca Park in 1915, this work of art featuring 48 poplar wood sculptures was moved in 1926 to another Irondequoit location. What is this popular piece?

132. This Rochesterian co-starred with Judy Carne in *Love On A Rooftop* and with Sally Field in *Gidget*.

133. Who always ended their program with the words ". . . and don't forget to be neighborly"?

134. According to the U.S. Government, the next one on Rochester television would be "61." The next what?

135. In February 1978, a crowd of 15,000 celebrated this occasion, basking in unusual 60-degree temperatures, and oohing and aahing as highwire artist Obondo highwired it 5 stories above Main Street. What was the occasion?

136. It was Rochester's first radio station, signing on the air in 1922.

137. Former Rochester Amerk play-by-play announcer Nick Nickson Jr. now does that job for the NHL Kings. In the summer months, though, he's the public address announcer at a major league ball park. Which one?

138. He hosted Rochester's only nightly television stock market report.

139. She starred in *Operation Madball* with Jack Lemmon, and played Clark Gable's wife in *Run Silent, Run Deep*. Rochesterians called her "Our Mary."

140. This Rochesterian was named "Composer-Arranger of the Decade" by *Cashbox* magazine for the 1970's.

ENTERTAINMENT

141. This product was first publicly demonstrated locally in the television/radio department of Sibley's downtown store in June of 1954.

142. In 1981, the fine for doing this on a city bus was $150 or 15 days in jail. Name the crime.

143. In the 60's, he hosted the WOKR-TV children's show, *The Funny Company*.

144. For decades, Henry Clune's column in the *Democrat and Chronicle* was required reading for true Rochesterians. What was the column titled?

145. This TV comedy giant of the 50's and 60's holds the record for the most mentions of our city's name on network TV.

146. Rochesterians with a taste for lexicography got their first crack at these, with pencils sharpened, in 1926.

147. Their only album, an Epic recording in 1969 was titled simply, *Introducing*.

148. What is the ice skating rink at Manhattan Square Park used for during the summer months?

149. Reporter Rich Newburg was the first to appear on WOKR-TV using this title for his investigative role.

150. During his own show, this disc jockey was told by jazz trumpeter Maynard Ferguson that he was "... one of the worst disc jockeys I've ever seen."

ENTERTAINMENT

151. This local news co-anchor pair ended up co-anchoring a marriage, becoming America's first such couple on TV. About getting married, she said, "I might as well. He's the only man I see on weekends." Who were they?

152. Rochester photographer Louis Ouzer has gained world fame for his powerful portraits of these subjects. Who are they?

153. Brothers Chuck and Gap Mangione first performed together under what name?

154. He left his morning show on WBBF in 1966 and went to Hollywood, starring in a short-lived series called *Mothers-in-law*.

155. Cornelia War's book, *How*, was so popular, it was first published in 1886, and reprinted 7 years later. What was *How* about?

156. An unknown working as a cook and porter, Edward House lived on Grieg Street for 35 years. But in 1965 he was rediscovered as a legend from the 20's and 30's. Who was he?

157. Rochester's Polish Club is named after what bird?

158. It combined with the *Chronicle* in 1870.

159. Who anchored the WOKR news before Dick Burt and Don Alhart?

160. His number one television show introduced America to Leslie Uggams and Irene Cara, who would later gain *Fame*.

161. Rochesterian Mary Frickett played Eleanor Roosevelt opposite Ralph Bellamy's FDR in this classic stage production.

162. Monroe County owns and operates three public golf courses. Name them.

163. *Snuff* prompted the arrest of four protesting women in Rochester. What was *Snuff*?

164. In 1949, Homer Bliss was the first to do this on Rochester television. It was broadcast on WHAM-TV from the stage of the Chamber of Commerce.

165. Rochester actress Marilyn Erskine played "Ida," the wife of actor Keefe Braselle, in this autobiographical movie. What was the title of the movie?

166. First thought of as a sport, this old favorite of circus shows was invented right here in Rochester by Nick Kaufmann and Wilford Barber in 1893.

167. Throughout the 1970's their sellout concerts were annual events at the Eastman Theatre.

168. This Rochester recording artist had to sign a pre-marriage contract, promising his fiancee that he would legally change his name for the sake of their future children.

169. What was the original name of The Playpen nightclub?

170. In the mid-60's he was the anchorman when WHEC overtook WROC's years of domination as the city's #1 news station.

171. Since 1975, "Uncle Roger" has been the midnight man on WCMF, playing progressive rock. What's his last name?

172. Mike Morgan, Ed Hasbroeck, Jack Kinnicutt, and Ed Ferland have this in common.

173. Despite the boom in the supplying industry, this practice was still unheard of inside the Rochester home, into the 20th century.

174. This Scottsville girl, once a waitress at the Hof Brau House, kicked up her heels as the dancing star of *Ziegfeld's Follies* of 1928.

175. Despite its rich musical history, the Eastman School has graduated only two Grammy-winning recording artists. Name them.

176. Formerly from Webster, she now hails from parts unknown as the TV-set-smashing lead singer of the *Plasmatics*.

177. Former Rochesterian Bob Balser was director *and* animator for this 1967 rock fantasy film.

178. This Marshall High grad starred in the TV series *The Big Valley* and in *Black Saddle*.

179. Franklin High grad Romolo DeSpirito went on to star at the Met. He was also the understudy to Enzio Pinza in this well-known musical.

180. A novice in 1947, he now holds the record among local TV broadcasters for the longest continuous on-the-air career.

ENTERTAINMENT

181. By the turn of the century, Rochester's 4 newspapers had all lined up to each represent the view of a political party. Which party did the *Democrat and Chronicle* support?

182. For years, Matt Rinaldi hosted WOKR's AM *Rochester* program. Before that, he appeared on the *Louise* show. What did he do before TV?

183. It resulted from the merger of the *Union Advertiser* and the *Evening Times* in 1918.

184. He was the local host of *The Mickey Mouse Club*.

185. In the summer of 1977, Rochesterians lined the Genesee downtown for a concert of broadcast rock music and an event in the sky. Clear skies, though, prevented it from being seen across the city as advertised. What was it?

186. New York State's oldest continuously running community theater closed its doors here in 1984, with a final production of *Spoon River Anthology*. Name the theater group.

187. *Foreigner*'s Lou Gramm is a bona fide rock superstar. But in the 70's, as Louis Grammatico of Gates-Chili, he sang and drummed for a Rochester group that never quite achieved that national fame. Name the group.

188. This Syracuse-born playwright, author of *Requiem for a Heavyweight*, was a four-pack-a-day smoker. That, and a family history of heart trouble, caught up with him as he died in the Strong Memorial operating room on June 28, 1975. Name him and his most famous TV work.

189. Rochesterian Lanny Frattare was a WBBF newsman and play-by-play man for the Amerks on WROC. He now does the "color" for a major league ball club. Which one?

190. After 22 years in newspaper, he became Rochester's most listened to radio news voice.

ENTERTAINMENT

191. How tall is Chuck Mangione without his hat?

192. These two performers share the War Memorial record for the fastest sellout of concert tickets.

193. While this ad man and producer coined the phrase, "No bah-dah-bees," his biggest claims to fame may be the theme music to HBO *Films*, *The CBS Movie* theme, and other network music scores.

194. What is actor Robert Forster's real name?

195. He's best known for his rendition of a Judy Garland classic.

196. In the early days of local television, WHEC and WVET-TV had something in common. What?

197. Once a year, Eastman Kodak participates in a televised nation-wide competition, and usually comes home with an award. What's the event?

198. On Rochester radio since 1958, he's billed himself as "The World's Tallest Midget."

199. In the 1920's William Abbott and his brother ran Rochester's Corinthian Theater. Twenty years later, with a partner named Lou, he'd be a theatrical star of his own, going by this name.

200. He hailed from Geneva, but Wilmer and his group drove Rochesterians wild with his song, "Give Me One More Chance." What was Wilmer's full name?

ENTERTAINMENT

201. This 1950 Aquinas grad left WBBF for a Hollywood career and became the original "Mr. Goodwrench" of TV commercial fame.

202. In the "Summer of Love," they walked through the audience, unnoticed, and up on stage to perform their "psychedelic" music at the Eastman Theatre.

203. Bernie Newmark and "The Moose" have delivered ski reports on WHAM radio since 1978. Who or what is "The Moose"?

204. In 1919 these were banned on Lake Ontario beaches by the city government.

205. This Rochester toastmaster broadcast the play-by-play as the Royals took on the Knicks at Madison Square Garden in the 1951 NBA Championship.

206. This radio promotion began along the banks of the Genesee in the summer of 1974.

207. Rush-Henrietta grad Jeff Wheat has been behind the camera for many network shows and movies. He's also been type-cast in the films *Neighbors* and *In Pursuit of DB Cooper*, and in TV's *Lou Grant*. What part has he always played?

208. The Riviera Theater opened in 1926 with the showing of an Artists Productions comedy short that is still seen on TV re-runs today.

209. What do the call letters of WXXI stand for?

210. She was known as "The Honeybee" when she worked on WBBF. Her next major job would be as an anchorwoman in Philadelphia.

ENTERTAINMENT

211. In 1949, police asked Rochester Telephone to shut off services to 13 downtown businesses. What kind of business were they all in?

212. WHAM radio signed on the air July 11, 1922, with a live musical performance. What instrument was played?

213. During the 1980 season, this television "color" man was canned by Lancer management for "negative reporting."

214. Bill Cosby "rediscovered" him in Las Vegas; Perry Como, in a golf tournament. Both helped launch his second TV career in 1972.

215. On February 13, 1974, Mark decided to return to church, and kissed Laurie goodbye. WHEC-TV was flooded with 400 phone calls in one day. Why?

216. In 1921, "Chicago," "Camel Walk," and "Washington Johnny" were all banned in Rochester. What were they?

217. In the wake of *Hullabaloo* and *Shindig*, WOKR-TV broadcast a weekly dance/music show called *It's Happening Now*. Who was the host?

218. It is a Rochester spring tradition that began in May of 1908.

219. U of R history professor Christopher Lasch wrote what is often regarded as the definitive work on the "me decade" of the 70's. What's the book titled?

220. This CBS play-by-play man was the voice of the Red Wings for one season in 1953, on WVET.

ENTERTAINMENT

221. Chief of Police William Lombard took the stage of the War Memorial on November 1, 1965, trying to end this band's show because of its "lewd and suggestive behavior."

222. Long before Slim Whitman became the rage, this Kodak secretary would hit the stage at the Grand Ole Opry and build a 25-year career on yodeling.

223. Henry Majauskas survived a helicopter crash in 1980 and took to the streets instead. Since then, he's never given Rochester radio listeners a bum steer. What's his radio name and current employer?

224. During her 16 years in Rochester, this poet, playwright, and recording artist gained her fame with the works *Letters To Young Sisters*, *Ebony Roses*, and other calls for black dignity.

225. He was the first voice of the Rochester Red Wings on WHEC radio.

226. What was the title of the book based on the actual murder trial of Sister Maureen?

227. It has been reported heard as far away as Haapavesi, Finland . . . Brisbane, Australia . . . and Waverly, Nebraska.

228. Brighton-born Richard Ben Cramer gained national attention for his in-depth look at some mysterious events surrounding a rock-n-roll singer he dubbed "The Killer." Who was the singer?

229. 3,500 people were on hand for the grand opening of the Eastman Theatre on Labor Day, 1922. What was on-stage at the Eastman that day?

230. He began by traveling the country trying to sell recordings of the sounds of Air Force bases to servicemen. Unsuccessful, he got his first break producing the *Focus* program on WOKR-TV in 1971.

ENTERTAINMENT

231. This popular parlor game gave Rochesterians their first look into the future with a YES, NO, or GOODBYE in 1920.

232. Rabbi Phillip Bernstein's book, *What Jews Believe,* began as an article in this national magazine in 1950.

233. He replaced Tom Decker as anchorman on WROC-TV news in 1975.

234. On a cold Sunday morning in November of 1980, hundreds of Rochesterians gathered near the intersection of Main and St. Paul. What had they come to witness?

235. This silent movie star's fame faded with the advent of talkies. Since then, she's lived in Rochester, a recluse.

236. In 1969 this station debuted what it called "The Sound Of The Underground," by playing the music of Jimi Hendrix, *Cream*, and the *Jefferson Airplane*.

237. He borrowed his slogan, "Have a happy," from a weathergirl on WCBS-TV. On the day she died, he stopped using it, until a friend of hers told him that she would have wanted him to continue saying it.

238. Ben Franklin grad Gene Cornish became lead guitarist for this group that had no fewer than 10 top-ten hits in the 60's, including the #1 hit, "Good Lovin'," in 1966.

239. What television show starred Miss Rita and the "Do-Bee"?

240. He began sketching while in the Marines, and his wife sold some of his first works in the late 1960's. His first showing was in Newport, Rhode Island, in 1968.

ENTERTAINMENT

241. She was hired and later fired by Arthur Godfrey. This singer was known to friends in Rochester as Lucille Ann Ciminelli.

242. This theater group stages all its performances in the Xerox Auditorium.

243. Weathercaster John Hambleton and sportscaster Rich Funke of WHEC both left Rochester for bigger markets, only to return. To what cities did they go?

244. *Foreigner*'s hit "Rev On The Red Line" is about what Charlotte phenomenon?

245. They co-anchored the ill-fated hour-long WHEC-TV newscast that went off the air March 14, 1980.

246. Jeff Tyzik, an accomplished performer on his own, has also written musical arrangements for this nightly network TV show.

247. Former City Councilman Chris Lindley was the captain of this U of R "team" that made its way to an appearance on network TV in 1962. What was the "sport"?

248. It was picketed in 1969 for showing the film *The Vixens*. Protesters complained of several scenes with "continuously exposed breasts."

249. In 1969 and 1970 this local band became only the second white rock group to record on the Motown Rare Earth record label.

250. This legendary actress came to Rochester to perform in the Lyceum Stock Theater troupe but was dropped by director George Cukor in the mid-20's.

251. The call letters of this Rochester station pay tribute to local radio and electronic pioneer Lawrence Hickson.

252. On September 23, 1978, Bob Dylan brought his show to the Rochester War Memorial. What was the show called?

253. Rochesterian Samuel Hopkins Adams wrote the stories that would become the films *Flaming Youth*, starring Clara Bow, and *It Happened One Night*. Who starred in that picture?

254. Technically, the city owned it when one day in 1981 it showed *Barbie's Fantasies*.

255. He was the director of the Eastman School of Music for nearly 50 years.

256. She was the host and star of the *Mohawk Showroom* broadcast on WHAM-TV in 1949.

257. This book by Curt Gerling took jabs at Rochesterians' general feeling of contentment.

258. Rochesterians in the late 1850's took part in a new fad, "surprise parties." But they weren't surprise parties as we know them today. Why?

259. *The Good Die Poor* was supposed to star Bette Davis and Humphrey Bogart, but the film was never made. Who was the Rochester newspaperman who penned the original book?

260. This star of the series *Family* was a charter member of the Henrietta Hayloft Theater troupe, and married her co-star in Rochester in the 50's.

ENTERTAINMENT

261. *Duke Jupiter* released their first album on Mercury Records in 1976. It featured the songs "Trouble In Paradise" and "Sweet Cheeks". What was the album title?

262. What is the comedian Sky Sands' real name?

263. Between 1908 and 1921, Pablo Casals, Enrico Caruso, and Arturo Toscanini all performed on the stage of this downtown building.

264. He holds the distinction of being the only person to work for all three Rochester TV news departments: WROC, WOKR, and finally, WHEC; not always by choice.

265. His show on WBFB-FM was hyperbolically billed as "Simon's Super Scintillating Sunshine Show."

266. He was the Atlantic Weatherman and delivered the report wearing a gas station attendant's uniform, complete with bow tie.

267. In the early morning hours of July 26, 1967, teenaged girls camped out to be first in line for tickets to see Mike, David, Peter, and Mickey. What was the collective name of these guys?

268. In 1885, entrepreneurs staged a re-enactment of the Civil War to raise funds for a memorial statue that still stands downtown. Which one?

269. After a stormy reception as Rochester's first "weathergirl" in 1975, Marcia Ladendorff moved on to other local broadcasting jobs. What were they?

270. In 1972, the *Rolling Stones*, Aretha Franklin, and *Sly & the Family Stone* all shared one distinction in common concerning the city of Rochester. What was it?

ENTERTAINMENT

271. In his career, this versatile man has chronicled crime and police for TV news. He's also been one of the city's most authoritative voices on jazz. He's even sold gas and heating oil on television from atop tanks near the airport.

272. In 1973, Hilton school teacher Teri Hartman decided that she could outperform the actors in the educational films she showed her classes. She's been on TV locally ever since. What does she do?

273. At 16, Brighton High student Sandy Balch was working behind the counter at Dunkin Donuts on Monroe Avenue; 21 years later she'd star behind a counter on a Broadway set in *Pump Boys & Dinettes*. What's her stage name?

274. While a student at St. Lawrence University, this Hollywood giant worked at the Rochester Steel Company plant, cutting sheets for cans in the summer of 1939.

275. He was the alleged subject of Henry Clune's book, *By His Own Hand*.

276. It began in Rochester on March 1, 1922, from inside the Times-Union Building.

277. In 1980, Chuck Mangione staged an all-night benefit featuring Dizzy Gillespie and Chick Corea. What cause did this benefit support?

278. Where do you "always know your neighbor; always know your pal"?

279. In 1850 Rochesterians were thrilled by Scandinavian Jenny Lind. What did she do?

280. Doc and Katie Abraham have been synonymous with the radio and TV show *The Green Thumb*. But what's Doc's real name?

281. At George's request, these sounds filled the Eastman House every morning, from the moment he awoke until he left for work.

282. After their song "Give Me One More Chance," *Wilmer & the Dukes* had another hit. Name this remake of a *Steve Miller Band* song.

283. Alice Cannon, daughter of Rabbi Phillip Bernstein, drew raves as "The Girl" in an off-Broadway production that's become a favorite of amateur theater because of its simple set and small cast. Name the show.

284. What instrument does Chuck Mangione play, and what does he refer to it as?

285. This obstreperous orchestra has in its brief history employed the services of Amerk Coach Mike Keenan, the *Polish Cowboy*, the *Pointed Sisters* [sic], and Simeon Smith. Its Telex number is Beechwood 45 789.

286. Known later as *Ferguson, David and Jones*, these Franklin High grads had a hit in 1968 titled "Breakin' Down the Walls of Heartache." Name the band.

287. His all-night jazz show was titled *The Best of All Possible Worlds*.

288. Nazareth Academy grad Laurie Johnson went on to become lead singer for this "Big Band," usually thought of in connection with Bob Hope.

289. According to station manager Karl Schub on the ill-fated network show *Buffalo Bill*, how far east does "The Bill Bittinger Show" television signal carry?

290. When she started at WHAM radio, her boss convinced Margaret Gribbroek to change her name to something simpler. She's been using this more pronounceable name in media ever since. Who is she?

291. Mabel Boll, the daughter of a city bartender, gained world acclaim as a glamour girl of the Roaring 20's. Her nickname was "The Queen." But of what?

292. What is the color of Duayne Hatchett's sculpture located in front of the Federal Building on State Street?

293. Of his first New York exhibit, *Town and Country* magazine wrote: ". . . the dramatic fantasy of Chagall, the wit of Toulouse-Lautrec, and the tenderness of Modigliani."

294. Rochesterian Steve Gadd is the most "in demand" studio drummer in America. His most widely seen and heard work was for a three-million-dollar 1981 reunion concert in Central Park. Who were the concert's stars?

295. This husband of a Rochester news woman hosted a children's television show called *Gizmo.*

296. This was the name for Don Potter's nightclub opened in the Rochester Club on East Avenue.

297. What phrase did Al Sigl use to begin every radio newscast?

298. What were the two things you needed to know if Anne Keefe called you for her *Cash Call* program?

299. This Rochesterian became a matinee idol starring in *A Foreign Affair* with Marlene Dietrich and *The Perils of Pauline* with Betty Hutton.

300. Although he never graduated from the Eastman School, this Rochesterian went on to compose classic songs for Frank Sinatra, the *Mills Brothers* and Sarah Vaughan to name a few.

ENTERTAINMENT

301. Rochesterian Joe English gained first fame drumming for the band *Jam Factory* of Syracuse. Years later, he'd become a member of a group featuring an ex-Beatle. Name the group and its "pre-English" album.

302. How many membership drives and auctions (combined) does WXXI-TV stage in a year?

303. Rochester band leader Len Hawley is best remembered for his outdoor renditions of this stirring standard.

304. Two of her biggest films were *Love 'Em and Leave 'Em* and *The Diary of a Lost Girl.*

305. One of Alec Wilder's classic compositions was recorded by several artists. But the most well-known versions were sung by Jo Stafford and Tony Bennett. Name the song.

306. It began as the Greenwood Area Arts Festival in 1969. There were 13 exhibitors and 26 people in attendance. The event raised $56.00. What's it called today?

307. From Mercy High and the Community Players she went on to star in *The Two Of Us* with Peter Cook, and in *3 Girls 3* with Debbie Allen of *Fame.*

308. Julius Stoll and Herman Pfaeffler unveiled the *Abend-Post* in Rochester in 1882. What was it?

309. What do the letters "DKX" stand for in WDKX?

ENTERTAINMENT ANSWERS

1. *Bedtime for Bonzo*
2. *Friends and Love*
3. Monroe County Dome Arena
4. *The Rochester Diet*
5. Chuck Connors
6. Bottom of the Bucket But
7. *The Family Rosary for Peace*
8. Tom Decker
9. *Cinderella Weekend* with Ross Weller
10. The waltz
11. Pan-African Cultural Exposition
12. The *Brass Buttons*
13. Talking motion picture
14. Cab Calloway
15. Wilson
16. The Pythodd
17. Tommy Long
18. Mickey Rooney
19. Ossie Sussman
20. *The Book of Mormon*
21. *Tic Tac Dough*
22. A United States weather report
23. WEZO-FM
24. War Memorial & Silver Stadium. He's the official Amerk and Red Wing organist!
25. Don Alhart
26. Rudolph Valentino
27. Bingo
28. Magic Mountain
29. The *Lawrence Welk Orchestra*
30. *The Honeymooners*; Art Carney
31. Lakeshore Boulevard
32. *Bishop Kearney Marching Kings*
33. Ron DeFrance
34. Labor Day Parade
35. Empire Drive-In
36. Comic Strips
37. Jack Rabbit and Wild Mouse
38. Danny Thomas
39. 60's rock groups
40. Six
41. WNYR disc jockey Tim Kincaid
42. Midge Costanza
43. *The Exorcist*
44. Crowley
45. Mitch Miller

ENTERTAINMENT ANSWERS

46. *Playing for Time*
47. William Warfield
48. David Bowie
49. "Give It All You Got"
50. Wyoma Best
51. *Dark Shadows*
52. Georges
53. *Saturday Night Fever*
54. WBBF disc jockeys Nick Nickson, Joe Deane and Leon Marguerite
55. *Fear No Evil*
56. Skipper Sam
57. *The Glory That Was Grease*
58. Mt. Hope Cemetery
59. FM, 2 to 1
60. Buffalo Bill
61. Maxwell's Silver Hammer
62. The flute
63. The *Grateful Dead*
64. Robert Forster
65. Gina Lollobrigida
66. Televised political debate
67. Tobogganing
68. *Chiller Theater*
69. Sibley, Lindsey & Curr
70. Peter Frampton
71. Starlite, Lakeshore, Washington and Rochester
72. German prisoners of war
73. Theda Bara
74. *Opinion Program*
75. Jay Silverheels; Tonto
76. Watergate hearings
77. The Blue Angels precision jet team
78. Under the Manger Hotel marquee
79. *Hawaii Five-O*
80. Carole Clifford
81. "I'd Rather Be In Rochester"
82. Joe Cullinane
83. No; the closest they came was a show at Toronto's Maple Leaf Stadium.
84. Motion picture theater
85. The Penny Fund
86. Downtown Holiday Inn
87. WAXC
88. Ronald Reagan
89. Brown Square
90. Barbara Rodgers, Lauren Dixon, Kimberly Adams
91. Blood (600 pints)

ENTERTAINMENT ANSWERS

92. Miniature golf courses
93. Trudy McNall
94. Swan boats
95. Hylie Morris' Alley
96. Over the Falls
97. *My Fair Lady*
98. Zane Grey
99. Rochester Oratorio Society
100. Duke Jupiter, "I'll Drink To You"
101. Tea dances
102. Roberta Quinlan
103. Playing Ilsa in *Casablanca* (Ingrid Bergman)
104. To make sound effects for silent films
105. Bishop Fulton J. Sheen
106. Bausch & Lomb
107. Hugh O'Brian (Wyatt Earp)
108. *True Stories of the New York State Police*
109. Liberace
110. "That's as far as I go."
111. Portrayed Brother Dominic in Xerox commercials
112. T-V Day (the debut of TV sets in Rochester stores)
113. Harvest Queen
114. "The Hump"
115. Don Michael Girard
116. Tennis
117. TV POWWW
118. Uncle Eddie
119. Foster Brooks
120. Gregory Peck
121. A Christmas tree
122. Robert Forster
123. Jack Slattery & George Haefner
124. A radio
125. *Where The Action Is*
126. Harmony
127. Linda Hill-Josh
128. *The New York Times*
129. 5 and 6
130. Mark Wolf
131. The merry-go-round at Sea Breeze
132. Peter Deuel
133. Doc and Katy Abraham
134. Channel; the next slot available from the FCC
135. The first "I Love Downtown" Celebration
136. WHQ
137. Dodger Stadium (Los Angeles)
138. Mort Nusbaum ("How's Business?")

ENTERTAINMENT ANSWERS

139. Mary LaRoche
140. Chuck Mangione
141. Color television
142. Playing a "big box" radio
143. Dan Morgan
144. "Seen and Heard"
145. Jack Benny (with his valet, Rochester!)
146. Newspaper crossword puzzles
147. Bat McGrath and Don Potter
148. Roller skating
149. The Troubleshooter
150. WHAM's Harry Abraham
151. Carole Clifford and Andy Anderson
152. Great musicians at the Eastman
153. The *Jazz Brothers*
154. Jerry Fogel
155. Etiquette and manners
156. Son House; legendary blues folk singer
157. Falcon
158. The *Democrat* newspaper
159. Ray Laws; also the station's first news director
160. Mitch Miller
161. *Sunrise at Campobello*
162. Durand-Eastman, Genesee Valley and Churchville
163. A pornographic movie featuring scenes of mutilation
164. Read the news
165. *The Eddie Cantor Story*
166. Acrobatic bicycling
167. Ferrante and Teicher
168. Jeff (Tkazyik) Tyzik
169. The Varsity Inn or "V.I."
170. Dick Tobias
171. McCall
172. All have hosted WHAM's *Opinion Program.*
173. Smoking
174. Clare Luce
175. Chuck Mangione (1976 and '78), William Warfield (1980)
176. Wendy O. Williams
177. *Yellow Submarine*
178. Peter Breck
179. *South Pacific*
180. Warren Doremus
181. The Republicans
182. He was a WBBF disc jockey.
183. The *Times-Union*
184. Jerry Carr
185. Projected laser images

ENTERTAINMENT ANSWERS

186. Rochester Community Players
187. *Black Sheep*
188. Rod Serling's *The Twilight Zone*
189. Pittsburgh Pirates
190. Al Sigl
191. 5'6"
192. Elvis Presley and Billy Joel
193. Ferdinand J. Smith
194. Robert Foster
195. Don Potter; "Somewhere Over the Rainbow"
196. They both shared the television Channel 10!
197. The Rose Bowl Parade (Kodak's float entry)
198. Jack Slattery
199. Bud Abbott (Abbott & Costello)
200. Wilmer Alexander Jr.
201. Paul Napier
202. *Jefferson Airplane*
203. Bernie's pet Chihuahua
204. One-piece bathing suits
205. Jerry Flynn
206. WBBF Raft Race
207. A cameraman
208. *Our Gang*
209. The Roman numeral 21
210. Jessica Savitch
211. Horse betting parlors
212. A piano, by Raymond Wilson of the Eastman School
213. Simeon Smith
214. Foster Brooks
215. After 20 years, *Secret Storm* went off the air!
216. Dances
217. Jack Palvino
218. Lilac Sunday
219. *The Culture of Narcissism*
220. Jack Buck
221. *The Rolling Stones*
222. Pat Torpey
223. Officer Hank, 990-WNYR
224. Nancy Dupree
225. Gunnar Wiig
226. *The Unholy Child*
227. WHAM
228. Jerry Lee Lewis; Cramer alleges Lewis may have killed his wife.
229. A movie; *The Prisoner of Zenda*
230. Al White
231. The Ouija board
232. *Life*

ENTERTAINMENT ANSWERS

233. Keith Martin
234. The demolition of the Commerce Building
235. Louise Brooks
236. WCMF-FM
237. Bob Mills
238. The *Young Rascals*
239. *Romper Room*
240. Ramon Santiago
241. Lu Ann Simms
242. The Blackfriars
243. New Orleans and Miami, respectively
244. Drag racing on Lake Avenue
245. Gabe Dalmath and Margaret Graham-Smith
246. The *Tonight Show*
247. G.E. *College Bowl*
248. The Riviera Theater
249. The *Rustix*
250. Bette Davis
251. WHEC-TV (Hickson Electric)
252. *The Rolling Thunder Revue*
253. Clark Gable and Claudette Colbert
254. The Riviera Theater; the city had foreclosed for back taxes.
255. Dr. Howard Hanson
256. Roberta Quinlan
257. *Smugtown* U.S.A.
258. The partygoers showed up at the house of the one to be surprised.
259. Henry Clune
260. Sada Thompson
261. *Sweet Cheeks*
262. Skylar Sands
263. The Naval Armory (new home of GEVA Theater)
264. Toby Gold
265. Simon Pontin
266. Homer Bliss
267. The *Monkees*
268. The Civil War Memorial in Washington Square Park
269. A news reporter for Channels 8 and 13
270. All three were officially banned from performing in the War Memorial.
271. Will Moyle
272. Television commercials
273. Cass Morgan
274. Kirk Douglas
275. George Eastman
276. Rochester radio; first heard on WHQ
277. Italian earthquake victims
278. "On the Erie Canal"
279. Sang opera

ENTERTAINMENT ANSWERS

280. George
281. Pipe organ music
282. "Living in the USA"
283. *The Fantastiks*
284. Flugelhorn; "honker"
285. *Nik & the Nice Guys*
286. The *Bandwagon*
287. Harry Abraham
288. *Les Brown's Band of Renown*
289. "About as far as Rochester"
290. Maggie Brooks
291. Diamonds
292. Yellow
293. Ramon Santiago
294. *Simon and Garfunkel*
295. Bob Keefe
296. The Musik Room
297. "Howdy neighbors!"
298. The count and the amount
299. John Lund
300. Alec Wilder
301. *Band on the Run*, Paul McCartney & *Wings*
302. Four
303. "The Star-Spangled Banner"
304. Louise Brooks
305. "Who Can I Turn To?"
306. The Corn Hill Arts Festival
307. Mimi Kennedy
308. The longest running German newspaper in city history
309. Frederick Douglass, Martin Luther King and Malcolm X

310. In 1834-Rochester, these people were compelled to register themselves in a book that was open to public inspection. Who were they?

311. In 1892, the city police tried a new mode of transportation. What was it?

312. It lasted for two hours on the night of November 9, 1965.

313. During December of 1944, the city imported German prisoners of war for this seasonal job.

314. When named in 1979, at 41 years old, he was the nation's second youngest.

315. Some 450 Rochesterians all spent the Christmas of 1950 in another country. Where were they?

316. The second Women's Rights Convention was held in Rochester in 1848. Among the resolutions was one calling for the removal of a word from the marriage ceremony. What word?

317. What was the cause of the Holiday Inn fire of 1978?

318. This 1934 event was broadcast over WHAM to the entire NBC radio network.

319. What does the "B" in Susan B. Anthony stand for?

320. What was the name given to anti-war activitists on trial for protest activities in Rochester in 1971?

321. In 1980, 123 people contracted food poisoning after a lunch of chicken livers and macaroni salad. Where had they eaten?

322. In 1887, 1,000 Rochesterians simultaneously took their phones off the hook and left them there for 18 months. Why?

323. One of the nasty side effects of local Prohibition, these deaths increased from 3 in 1918, to 25 by 1925. What was the cause of death?

324. Speaking before 20,000 Rochesterians in October '76, candidate Jimmy Carter ended his speech by doing something unusual, and then explaining it. What was it that he did?

325. Sixteen Rochesterians were put under constant surveillance during World War II. Why?

326. In 1961, he was elected the city's first Italian mayor.

327. Nathaniel Rochester left his Maryland home with 10 of these, but let them go by the time he reached the Genesee valley.

328. According to the 1960 census, how many of the county's 19 towns had a white population of 95% or higher?

329. Triggered by the launch of Sputnik, Irondequoit High School was first in Monroe County to offer this course in 1960.

330. Nathaniel died before Rochester became a city. Did the city ever have a Mayor Rochester?

331. 4,000 people owed the city one million dollars in 1978. For what?

332. This was cut instead of a ribbon to formally open the George Eastman House in 1949.

333. During a snowstorm in the winter of 1981, Rochesterians lined Main Street for a parade. What was the occasion?

334. In the 1880's, Rochesterian Lewis Morgan wrote Ancient Society, a study of man's development from savage to civilization. It would become a handbook for Socialists as their dogma swept across Europe, and its reading was recommended by this man.

335. They were known, in 1840, as "The Watch," six elderly men with long sticks and lanterns.

336. In 1934, a nine-foot bronze statue was planned for downtown. But a site was never chosen, and the plan was dropped. Who would have been immortalized?

337. The Baden Street Settlement House, the city's first, opened in 1901, aiding poor Germans and Poles. What religious group set it up?

338. In 1980, the Rochester School Board revived this practice in its schools on a limited basis, with parental consent.

339. In 1928, the city posted a watchman in the Lincoln-Alliance Bank tower to scan the city skyline for violations of this law.

340. How many county managers has Monroe County had in its 48 years?

341. From 1840 through 1860, omnibusses were the main means of public transportation for Rochesterians. How were they powered?

342. This was the name given to those Rochesterians who supported and helped operate the Underground Railroad.

343. In 1901, Rochesterians paid $1 to get a number from Albany, but had to make their own.

344. When French explorers passed through our region, the Seneca Indians fed them beans and squash, but where was the beef? There were no cattle. What meat did they eat?

345. What was Susan B. Anthony's punishment for her "crime" of voting in 1872?

346. The Lewis Street Settlement was originally founded to teach American sanitary and housekeeping customs to a particular ethnic group. Which one?

347. In 1887, a woman fell outside Georgianna Sibley's eastside home. This incident led her to think that the hospital across the river was too far away, and she went out and paid to have one built closer to home. Which one?

348. In 1946, a local bartenders' union sought to ban women from "barmaid" jobs. Why did they want such a state law?

349. Called "the last of the heretics," Dr. Algernon Crapsey, an Episcopalian, was tried for his denial of this religious doctrine.

350. In 1912, there were 6 Rochesterians on board. Three of them died with some 1,500 others at sea.

351. In January of 1917, schools were closed down, and businesses were open only 4 days a week, with Mondays off. Prompted by the outbreak of World War I, this conservation move would save on what?

352. Jean Walrath, a newspaper movie critic and a Democrat, became the city's first in 1944.

353. In 1857, telegraph man Hiram Sibley tried connecting America with Russia, and advised the U.S. Secretary of State that some northern land was available for purchase. Name the land.

354. In 1850, Rochester opened a "Home for the Friendless," an alternative to prison. Who were sent there?

355. In the 1820's it was dubbed "The Young Lion of the West."

356. Why did U of R students protest the presence of Dow Chemical Corporation recruiters on their campus in 1967?

357. Deland Chemical, once the main industry of Fairport Village, was destroyed by fire in 1893. Before that, it was one of the nation's leading suppliers of this everyday household chemical.

358. For several evenings in the summer of '42, Rochesterians turned off all their lights. Why?

359. In 1970, feminists staged a protest of a War Memorial "Bridal Fair," sponsored by WBBF radio. What was their concern?

360. Stephen B. Story was Rochester's first in 1928, paid a salary of $20,000, as a new type of government came into being.

361. A large percentage of the blacks who migrated to Rochester in the 1960's came from the city of Sanford. What was the state?

362. Mohawk Flight 112 crashed at the Monroe County Airport in 1963, killing 7. What was the cause?

363. In the 1870's, a U of R science professor and leaders of the local Protestant Church squared off. What was the issue?

364. A man with his throat slashed was found lying by a road in 1823. He became the first official murder victim in Monroe County. In what town did this occur?

365. The first teacher strike in Monroe County took place in this town in 1971. 228 teachers temporarily chalked off the job.

366. Mother Hieronymo and three Sisters of Charity founded it across the street from the Bull's Head Tavern in 1857.

367. From 1921 to 1933, 57 boats were confiscated along Lake Ontario and sold at auction. Why?

368. How did Ebenezer Allan, builder of the area's first flour mill, get the nickname "Indian"?

369. Locally, the first one was performed at Strong Memorial Hospital in 1966, and it's still working.

370. This new squad was added to the police force in 1905 to keep a check on a budding new industry and its by-product.

371. Three women chained themselves to exam tables at Strong Memorial Hospital in 1978. What were they protesting?

372. Rochester police set up a "hot line" for tips in 1978. About what did they want information?

373. On September 6, 1901, some 7,000 Rochesterians traveled to Buffalo to view that city's Pan-American Exposition. They witnessed history there. What happened?

374. U of R professor Harry Gove proposed using Carbon-14 to authenticate what historic artifact?

375. Rochesterians were immunized in 1976 to prevent this illness.

376. In 1911, a state factory inspector visited 33 factories in Rochester looking for hazardous working conditions. How many of the 33 were able to pass inspection?

377. It is believed to be the oldest building in Monroe County.

378. Nearly 40 years before the recent Metro Police issue, county voters rejected a 1% sales tax and voted no in a referendum to support the construction of this.

379. In 1888, a group from Indiana known as "The White Caps" surfaced in Rochester. They specialized in threatening mail and back-alley beatings of some immigrants. What was their other name?

380. At the outbreak of World War I in 1914, some young Rochesterians went across the border to Canada. Why?

381. How many terms did Barber Conable serve in Congress?

382. In 1870, the Democrat newspaper threatened to publish the names of men who were committing this offense. Though it wasn't against the law, exactly, what was their offense?

383. Attempts to officially make Rochester a city were blocked by the fathers of which nearby rival city?

384. How did Rochester's "free schools" of the 1840's get their name?

385. It was Rochester's first synagogue, built in 1848.

386. In 1978, two upstaters were charged with conspiring to steal U.S. property and sell it for $200 million. What was it?

387. In 1941, Judge Harold Burke imposed the sentence of 6 months in a penitentiary. The charge would surface again, against others, 25 years later. And Burke would again pronounce sentence. What was the charge?

388. The arrival of Hemlock Lake water into city homes in 1875 made this household convenience possible.

389. Ninety Rochesterians were arrested on May 7, 1971. How were they breaking the law?

390. In 1908, a Lake Ontario steamboat sank following a collision with another near Charlotte Pier. Twenty-one passengers all escaped injury. There was no ice, but what was the name of this steamer?

391. In 1857, Rosetta Douglass became the last child who couldn't get in. To what?

392. In 1954, Rochesterians were amazed as darkness engulfed the city in the middle of the day. How come?

393. It was known as "The Royal Blue," and stopped at Union Hill, Williamson, and Wallington.

394. Mayor Joseph Leech was the honored guest at Rochester's centennial in 1934. He came overseas from what 2,000-year-old city?

395. One in every three Rochesterians owned one of these by 1930.

396. Dictator Benito Mussolini was on hand for the dedication of a structure built by George Eastman. What was it?

397. In 1932, the City of Rochester would not permit wives of city employees to hold city jobs as well. Why?

398. 1,423 children under the age of 14 were doing this in Rochester in 1920.

399. In its first creative approach to this problem, the city sold this to pig farmers in the 1880's.

400. In August of 1928, Dr. Henry Ogden warned the county's Board of Supervisors of an impending health problem that ended up haunting them for four decades. What was his warning?

401. In 1825, this cut the Rochester-to-New York City travel time from 6 weeks to 9 days.

402. They were first painted on city streets in 1914.

403. 10 died, 34 were injured on the day after Thanksgiving, 1978. How?

404. When Saul Alinsky was brought to Rochester to help in the organization of FIGHT, he left a university position in another city. What was the city?

405. Women's suffrage wasn't Susan B. Anthony's first "cause." What was?

406. How many mayors did Rochester have during the city's first ten years, from 1834 to 1843?

407. By 1860, many Rochesterians were known as "Wide-awakes." What were they doing to earn that title?

408. This New York governor was instrumental in funding the development of the National Technical Institute for the Deaf.

409. Clara Barton founded the second American chapter of this, right here in Rochester.

410. The city annexed it from Greece in 1916.

411. In 1893, the State of New York forced several local employers to let go German and Polish factory workers, 14 to 16 years old. Why?

412. There was a proposal in 1981 to level the entire Main Street block from Clinton to St. Paul and spend $40 million. To build what?

413. How were Rochester's street cars powered before the arrival of electricity in 1890?

414. In 1896, the speed limit was 8 miles per hour, and the fine for exceeding it was $2. What was the vehicle?

415. This form of government preceded the County Legislature.

416. In 1865, his funeral train passed through Monroe County on its journey westward.

417. More than 100 women, 31 with babies, arrived in Rochester to live in 1946. Why?

418. In 1920, this village was invaded by Rochester gangs, seeking to end a dispute over a woman, but creating a full-scale riot instead.

419. Some 30,000 Rochesterians took up home gardening in 1943. What was it they were growing?

420. During the Battle of Britain, a local company brought British children to Rochester to live. What were these children known as?

421. On October 22, 1981, this union walked off the job in Rochester and other cities. At their places of employment, though, it was business almost as usual, with no incidents. Who were they?

422. In November of 1929, a Rochester business leader declared before the Chamber of Commerce, "The worst is over." The worst of what?

423. Mayor Cutler banned public use of these as unsafe in July of 1904.

424. By 1895, a trip from the city to Summerville, via St. Paul Boulevard, would require you to make at least two stops. Why?

425. In 1929, the first president of the Irish Republic came to Rochester to visit his mother, Catherine Wheelwright, who lived on Brighton Street. Who was he?

426. Nathaniel Rochester journeyed here from what colonial state?

427. The Round Heads started the first one in Rochester in 1815.

428. In 1982, Monroe County reported the largest number of cases of this illness in New York State, outside of the New York City area.

429. It was three years before the city of Rochester's first one occurred in 1837.

430. The 1895 decision by Rochester barbers to close on Sundays was blasted by a newspaper editorial as a violation of a basic right? What right?

431. In the early nineteenth century, Rochester was producing 5,000 barrels of this a day.

432. Phys. ed. instructor Hazel Varner filed a $1.9 million suit against the University of Rochester in 1971. What was her charge?

433. In 1927, Frank, George, and Nigger made the last run. Who or what were they?

434. Frederick Douglass was once nominated and ran for public office in 1874, but he didn't win election to the local assembly. Which party's candidate was he?

435. In 1833, church sextons were fined if they did not ring their steeple bells whenever this happened.

436. Rochester's original Federal Building and New Bethel Church were two of the buildings simultaneously bombed on this holiday.

437. Now a U.S. Senator, this professor was brought in by Eastman Kodak in 1967 to negotiate a settlement with FIGHT for the hiring of blacks.

438. In the winter of 1819, he was paid $80 for the entire season, and only worked nights. What was his occupation?

439. What was the faith of the first preacher in Pittsford?

440. Governor Thomas Dewey was on hand for the 1954 grand opening ceremony held in Henrietta. What opened?

441. Monroe County was named in honor of this man.

442. In the 20's, a local scientist served his guests fruit juice mixed with laughing gas. What prompted this non-alcoholic kick?

443. After 6 years, former University of Rochester professor Edward Losansky was reunited with his wife in 1982. Where had she been?

444. In 1914, the Federation of American Zionists held their national convention in Rochester. In an important name change, the Daughters of Zion became known as what group?

445. Less than one-third of these in Rochester at first took advantage of their new right, finally granted to them by an act of Congress.

446. It held its first convention in 1965, with 1,500 delegates crowding into RIT's Ritter-Clark Gymnasium.

447. From 1970 through 1980, how many deaths per thousand people were there every year in Monroe County?

448. During the invasion of 1983, how many Rochesterians were among the students evacuated from Grenada?

449. He won county-wide election in 1970 with both Republican and Democratic endorsements.

450. On March 5th, 1930, several thousand gathered at Washington Square Park for a protest demonstration. What were they protesting?

451. Why did the city abolish 489 garbage collector and street sweeper jobs in 1946?

452. In 1982, a city official said of them, "What some can't handle in terms of strength, they make up for in coordination." Who were they?

453. Concerned with the prevailing Victorian attitudes about cigarettes, William Kimball ordered this 21-foot statue built and erected above his tobacco factory in 1885.

454. For how long did Rochester's racial riots of 1964 last?

455. It destroyed one home and damaged 40 others in the winter of 1974. What was it?

456. The Millerites gathered in Talman's Hall on March 21, 1844, for what event that never happened?

457. By 1880, many Italian immigrants did this work, causing bitter feelings that surfaced as discrimination for decades.

458. You can still hop into one in Atlantic City, but in Rochester they roamed the streets from 1914 to 1916.

459. Which came first, Blue Cross or Blue Shield?

460. At the turn of the century, it was the most popular night school course for Rochester's hard-working immigrants.

461. How many bishops has the Diocese of Rochester had from 1868, when it began, until 1984: a total of 116 years?

462. This east-west connection was built in 1862, at a cost of $15,000.

463. She died on March 13, 1906, in her home on Madison Street.

464. In 1919, John Frisbee made history going from Cobbs Hill to Main and Goodman. Why?

465. In February of '83, local veterans Robbie Stephenson and Gary Beikirch parachuted into California for a 100-mile marathon run. The goal: to attract attention to the Vietnam vet. Where did they run?

466. In 1978, these criminals were given an 8 p.m. to 8 a.m. curfew as a sentence. What was the charge?

467. In 1977, 300 Rochesterians piled into the tax office, claiming that they didn't need to pay taxes. Their reason?

468. Rochester's first electric streetcar had a route that began in the city and ended where?

469. The first local building for Christian worship was set up by French missionaries in 1721. The spot is now the site for Christian education on the city's east side. Name the school.

470. In 1949, for the first time, city police were able to use chemical testing for DWI convictions. What was used for testing?

471. In 1940, Rochesterians donated 1,500 of these to the British.

472. Three Rochesterians were aboard when the Germans sank her in 1915.

473. From 1919 to 1932, Louis Wehle closed the Genesee Brewery and opened a bakery. Why?

474. In 1917, Rochesterians of all faiths observed meatless Tuesdays. What prompted this?

475. Sam Patch's fateful daredevil jump into the Genesee was condemned by local clergy. Why?

476. Rochester's City Council moved to tear up abandoned trolley rails in 1941, rather than pave them over. Why?

477. In 1975, Monroe County had two more of these than it had marriages.

478. It happened for the first time in the village of Rochester on December 5, 1819, and no one knew how to stop it effectively.

479. He was the United States Minister to Haiti from 1889 to 1893.

480. The County Legislature voted to give Lucien Morin one for $5,000 in 1978.

481. 7,000 of these in the city were inspected in 1977. As many as 75% were not working.

482. Who carried Monroe County by 7,000 votes in the 1960 election, Nixon or Kennedy?

483. Rochester was known by another name in the 1820's. What was it?

484. The British contemplated invading Rochester in 1813, but decided against it. Where would the battle have been fought?

485. The University of Rochester played a key role in research for the Manhattan Project, the development of the atomic bomb. What aspect was extensively tested and researched here?

486. An 8-foot high, 100-foot long barrier was constructed on the Veterans Bridge in 1980 to protect pedestrians. From what?

487. The name of the organization FIGHT was an acronym formed from these words.

488. It reached its peak volume in the summer of '78 when 655 neighbors called to complain.

489. Rochesterians Don McCann and the brothers Kramb all died on the same day in December 1941. Why?

490. In 1979, a county jail inmate went to the State Supreme Court for permission to keep something in jail. What?

491. In the last quarter of the 19th century, Rochester's Polish and Russian Jews formed the Spinoza Literary Society for fellow countrymen in the city. What was a main purpose of the society?

492. In all the years of its existence, only one runaway was caught, and she killed herself rather than return to her point of origin. What was it?

493. In 1931, police arrested people for running a lottery where contestants had to predict the correct date and time for this gruesome event.

494. In 1877, it was the longest one, connecting City Hall with the reservoir at Hemlock Lake.

495. By 1864, some in Monroe County actually hired men to do this as substitutes for them.

496. St. Joseph's Catholic Church opened Rochester's first foreign language school in 1836. What was the language?

497. They made the rounds again along city streets in 1976.

498. The first bridge over the Genesee River, in what would become Rochester, is known by what name today?

499. In 1838, Rochester became the first city in the nation to form a society in opposition to this practice.

500. Did President James Monroe ever visit Monroe County?

501. Rochester barbers collected more than a quarter of a million of these during 1942 for the war effort.

502. In Rochester, in the late 1970's, he led a band of displaced Philadelphia revolutionaries known as "MOVE" who believed in, among other things, the consumption of raw chicken. His legal name was Vincent Leapheart, but he and his followers all shared this assumed last name.

503. The city's first mayor, Jonathan Child, quit. He gave up his mayoral post rather than succumb to pressure to license more of these businesses.

504. By 1920, city police were arresting more and more offenders dubbed "Hopheads." What was the crime?

505. When this 12-week strike ended on January 20, 1976, it produced the first local union contract at a private nursing home. Name the home.

506. At the turn of the century, businessman H.H. Warner offered a $100 prize to budding local astronomers. What did they have to do to win?

507. He landed here for a visit in 1927, just 2 months after making history.

508. One day in 1956, police cleared Broad and Exchange, fearing that the wind would knock down one of these, which weighed 400 pounds of aluminum.

509. President of the First National Bank of Rochester, she was America's first woman bank president in 1917.

510. The Monroe County Legislature once considered a garbage land-fill in this body of water.

511. At the turn of the century, Protestant sects actively competed in the recruiting of new immigrants in Rochester. Which sect had the largest congregation countywide?

512. Aviation experts have theorized that the storm that crash-landed Mohawk Flight 112 in 1963, might also have been the reason 36 people survived. How so?

513. In 1830, 680 people were in jail for crime that totalled $6,300. What was the crime?

514. It began at 9:28 a.m. on January 25, 1982.

515. He first lived in Dansville and Bloomfield before moving to the land along the Genesee in 1818.

516. Did President Kennedy ever come to Rochester during his term of office?

517. How much federal money was used to build the Erie Canal?

518. The 1932 election was a monumental one for local Democrats. They elected a Democrat in Albany, and another one in Washington. Name them.

519. This federal program first came to Rochester in 1936, when 203 elderly Rochesterians received their checks.

520. When Jonathan Child of the Whig Party was elected as the city's first mayor, what was the party's major platform issue?

521. Leonard Lipsky was only the second man in state history to be found guilty of murder under this unusual circumstance.

522. He hatched the nation's first fish hatchery, and today a road to a secluded fishing spot on the Genesee is named in his memory.

523. What substance was burned in city street lamps before gas or electricity?

524. Built in 1832, this was the first rural Catholic church in New York State.

525. As Polish immigrants moved into Rochester, a portion assumed names of another nationality to ease their assimilation into the community. What nationality?

526. A Supreme Court ruling finally permitted this in the county jail.

527. What was the cause of the Allegheny jet crash in 1979?

528. At the turn of the century, it was known as "The Coney Island of Western New York."

529. In 1943, Rochesterians were allowed to ring a replica of the Liberty Bell on the Main Street Bridge if they did this.

530. Why did Rochesterville's first newspaper go out of business?

531. These three "400-year-old visitors" pulled up for a stop at Charlotte in 1892.

532. The newly-founded town of Henrietta may have been the first in the county to enact a leash law in 1818. Owners were to be fined fifty cents for each animal found running at large. The law wasn't for dogs, though. For what animal was it?

533. In 1938, Rochester's mayor requested the installation of an anti-aircraft unit in the city. What event prompted that request?

534. These West Ridge Road homes were said to be the model for others all across America in the 1800's. What was their distinguishing feature?

535. It was again manufactured and sold locally on April 27, 1933, for the first time in nearly 14 years.

536. He was Monroe's first county clerk and president of the Bank of Rochester.

537. Upon its completion in the southern towns in 1919, the Barge Canal caused this to become obsolete.

538. This famous French explorer first canoed through Irondequoit Bay in 1669, as he moved toward America's midwest wilderness.

539. Invited to participate in 1983, this Rochester band boycotted New York's St. Patrick's Day Parade because a leader of the Irish Republican Army was appointed its grand marshall.

540. Rochester gave birth to this political party, a group dedicated to making public the rites and rituals of a membership lodge.

541. During World War II, hundreds of working Rochesterians were given "A" ration cards which limited the amount of gasoline they could get per week. What was the limit?

542. In 1899, U of R alumni were solicited for two fund drives. One, by Susan B. Anthony, would allow women to be taught at the school. The second, by the university itself, sought funds for a building construction. What would be built?

543. In 1894, the city organized a sidepath organization to collect a one dollar user fee to finance more sidepaths. Who were the users?

544. In 1836, it was the city's first, and was called the "Blue Eagle," a term that would re-surface 100 years later, after the Depression. What was it?

545. Both of these community agencies were formed in 1964, as a response to the summer's rioting.

546. At the start of the Civil War, where did Rochester's population rank with respect to Chicago's, Detroit's, and Cleveland's?

547. In 1934, passengers on the Ontario I car ferry from Rochester to Canada could pass the time by inserting coins into this amusement device.

548. Thirteen men helped Indian Allan build the area's first flour mill. When they finished, how did they celebrate?

549. Near the end of the 19th century he was known as the "father of American anthropology" for his studies of the Iroquois.

550. In 1891, over 100 varieties of the first ones were planted by John Dunbar in what is now Highland Park.

551. In the 1860's, Susan B. Anthony found herself at odds with the fledgling University of Rochester. What was the issue?

552. In 1970, more than 100,000 Rochesterians signed a petition protesting this U.S. action.

553. Who were Michelle Maenza, Carmen Colon, and Wanda Walkowicz?

554. On September 17, 1862, nearly 200 men from Rochester and the county, all members of the 108th Regiment, died in this Civil War battle that was known for its "Bloody Lane."

555. In 1966, FIGHT President Franklin Florence demanded that this company hire 600 unemployed during the next 18 months.

556. Had British or French explorers on the lake taken an interest in settling along the shore in the 1750's, most historians believe those settlements would have been in two cities other than Rochester. Where?

557. This method of traffic control is still used on some Caribbean resort islands, but in 1924 these were an everyday part of life for those who traveled Main Street.

558. According to her own confession, what was the true source of the "rappings" that Margaret Fox and her sister—the founders of Spiritualism—heard?

559. In 1833, more foreign money from this country was circulating in Rochester than money printed by the U.S. mint. Name the country.

560. The Catholic Church rejected the proposal of U of R's Dr. Harry Gove to test the authenticity of the Shroud of Turin. Why?

561. Before his death in 1981, William Bradley Griffin wrote, "The final disposition will be the murder of my person." Where did he die?

562. He published a newspaper called The North Star in 1847.

563. On June 30, 1946, fifty Rochesterians had "grandstand seats" in the Pacific. What event did they witness?

564. This was constructed to carry the Erie Canal water over the waters of the Genesee.

565. Which Rochester church was erected in memory of Nathaniel Rochester?

566. What specific incident is recorded as the start of the rioting in the summer of 1964?

567. This standard firefighting practice was first instituted officially in 1957.

568. He was the last Republican mayor of Rochester.

569. In 1970, it stood at 3.1%.

HISTORY

570. Believing that they would need her support, Susan B. Anthony rallied voters for this political party in 1872.

571. The brick homes and apartments that line the west end of Norris Drive in Cobbs Hill served a different purpose during the war. What were they?

572. It would be 42 years after Rochester became a city that this nationality would finally have its first two naturalized citizens living here.

573. Led by the Black Student Union, 200 co-eds at Monroe Community College protested alleged local activities of this group in 1980.

574. In 1940, Rochester area truck farms had 13% of their work forces made up of these people.

575. Nathaniel Rochester attempted to grow fruit trees not usually associated with this area. What was the fruit?

576. The jail first set aside cells for female prisoners in 1839. What were they charged with?

577. In the summer of 1928, federal agents fired 700 shots at a boater on the lake off Seabreeze. Why?

578. In 1979, did more county households earn $30,000-$35,000 or $20,000-$25,000?

579. In 1942, it included 29,323 Monroe County men between the ages of 20 and 45.

580. By 1833, 154 Rochesterians had died due to this.

581. What was "Operation Step-up"?

582. Delia Scrantom, wife of pioneer Hiram, was Rochester's first.

583. The Town of Irondequoit once had a village that was named after a city destroyed by Roman conquest. This village met a similar fate, but with natural causes. Name it.

584. Over the years, the east-west corridor cutting through the south end of the city has accommodated three modes of transportation. Name them.

585. President Thomas Jefferson told the planners of this man-made waterway that they were ". . . a century too soon."

586. Famed anthropologist Lewis Henry Morgan willed $80,000 for the education of women at the U of R in 1881. There was just one drawback. What was it?

587. In 1890, a wooden stump sat on the corner of Main and Franklin, with a collection cup beside it. The hope was to raise funds to build a new one. No one contributed. What would have been rebuilt?

588. The city put unemployed men to work at this job in 1894.

589. In 1890, the westside was proud of its "Four Corners." Not to be outdone, eastside merchants gave this name to their area of Main, North, Elm, Franklin, and East Avenue.

590. The "Great Blackout" that pitched Rochester into darkness was caused by sun spots, a power surge from Canada, or, we still don't know?

591. During the 1934 centennial celebration, an office in the Reynolds Arcade was set up to register citizens with proof. Proof of what?

592. Seneca Indians of the Iroquois tribe settled this region around 1300, fleeing from Canada. What were they running from?

593. On May 28, 1946, the City of Rochester closed for business. Why?

594. In 1969, black students at the U of R occupied this campus building, presenting seven demands to administrators.

595. In 1803, developer James Wadsworth offered 6 bushels of wheat, a barrel of whiskey, and a barrel of pork as the prize. What was the contest?

596. The Erie Canal was nicknamed "Clinton's Ditch" when it opened in 1825. Who was Clinton?

597. In 1912, a Democrat and Chronicle headline prematurely heralded the end of this profession in Rochester.

598. At the turn of the century, the city's library, museum, and historical society were all housed under the same roof in a converted building. What had the building been used for previously?

599. In 1969, black students at the Colgate Divinity School shut down the campus for 17 days, demanding the hiring of 4 black teachers and 10 black trustees. What was the outcome?

600. This "business" began with net cash assets on hand of $14.44.

HISTORY ANSWERS

310. Drunks; the book was called "The Habitual Drinkers List."
311. The bicycle
312. The Great Blackout
313. Shoveling snow
314. Bishop Matthew Clark
315. Fighting in Korea
316. "Obey"
317. Arson
318. Rochester's centennial celebration
319. Brownell
320. The Flower City Conspiracy
321. The Jewish Home where they were living
322. To protest a rate hike
323. Alcohol poisoning (drinking bootlegged liquor)
324. Hand-signed the word "love" for the hearing-impaired
325. They were Rochester's Japanese population.
326. Henry Gillette
327. Slaves
328. All of them
329. Russian
330. Yes, his son Thomas was Rochester's 6th mayor.
331. Outstanding parking tickets
332. A strip of film
333. The return of former hostage Colonel Thomas Schaeffer
334. Karl Marx
335. Rochester's first police "force"
336. Nathaniel Rochester
337. The Jewish congregation of Temple B'rith Kodesh
338. Paddling
339. Air pollution (emissions from smokestacks)
340. Three; Clarence Smith ('36-'60), Gordon Howe ('60-71), Lucien Morin ('71-'83)
341. By horses
342. Abolitionists
343. License plates
344. The French dined on cooked dog meat.
345. A fine, which she never paid
346. Italian women
347. Genesee Hospital
348. They wanted the jobs to go to returning male war veterans.
349. The virgin birth of Jesus Christ
350. The Titanic
351. Coal
352. Female political candidate
353. Alaska, Secretary Seward's "Folly"
354. Prostitutes
355. Rochester

HISTORY ANSWERS

356. Dow made napalm destined for use in Vietnam.
357. Baking powder
358. World War II blackout practice
359. The commercialization of marriage
360. City manager
361. Florida
362. A violent wind and rainstorm at take-off
363. Evolution
364. Parma, along Ridge Road
365. Spencerport
366. St. Mary's Hospital
367. They were rum-runners from Canada.
368. He "knew" many squaws in the Biblical sense.
369. Kidney transplant
370. Auto traffic squad
371. Abortion
372. Six organized crime bombings
373. President William McKinley was assassinated.
374. The Shroud of Turin
375. Swine flu
376. Two
377. Stone-Tolan House
378. The War Memorial
379. The Ku Klux Klan
380. To enlist and fight in the Canadian Army
381. Ten (20 years)
382. Girl-watching (making loud remarks as ladies passed by)
383. Canandaigua
384. There was no charge to attend.
385. B'rith Kodesh
386. A nuclear submarine, the USS Trepang
387. Draft dodging
388. Water closets (indoor plumbing)
389. They were protesting US involvement in Cambodia.
390. The Titania
391. An all-white city school; she was the daughter of Frederick, and her admission by the Board of Ed ended strict segregation.
392. A total eclipse of the sun; the next one—2254 A.D.!
393. The Rochester and Sodus Bay Railroad
394. Rochester, England
395. A car
396. The Eastman Dental Clinic in Rome, opened in 1932.
397. They'd be taking valuable work away from men during the Depression.
398. Working; the second highest child labor force in the state
399. Garbage
400. Lake Ontario was becoming polluted.

HISTORY ANSWERS

401. Erie Canal
402. Crosswalks
403. The Holiday Inn fire in Greece
404. Syracuse
405. Temperance
406. Ten; not a great deal of stability
407. Opposing slavery by enlisting in the Union Army
408. Hugh Carey; then a Congressman who obtained the federal funds
409. Red Cross
410. Charlotte
411. They couldn't read or write English.
412. A domed stadium
413. By horses
414. Bicycle
415. Board of Supervisors
416. Abraham Lincoln
417. They were war brides.
418. Fairport
419. Victory Gardens
420. "Kodakids"
421. Air traffic controllers
422. The Depression (it had just begun)
423. Fireworks
424. To pay tolls; two tollgates were set up along the route.
425. Eamonn de Valera
426. Maryland(Hagerstown)
427. Presbyterian church
428. Venereal disease
429. Murder
430. The right to a shave on Sunday
431. Flour
432. Sex discrimination
433. City of Rochester fire horses
434. Republican
435. A fire
436. (The) Columbus Day (Bombings)
437. Daniel P. Moynihan
438. Rochester's first policeman
439. Baptist (Reverend Daniel Brown)
440. The New York State Thruway
441. James Monroe, the fifth President
442. Prohibition
443. Held without visa in Russia
444. The Hadassah
445. Women voters
446. FIGHT
447. Eight

HISTORY ANSWERS

448. Three
449. Sheriff Al Skinner
450. Unemployment (the Depression)
451. They wanted to unionize
452. Prospective female firefighters
453. Mercury
454. Two days (three nights)
455. A Barge Canal break at Bushnell's Basin
456. The end of the world; they then said it would happen 10/22/44.
457. They were hired as strikebreakers.
458. Jitneys
459. Blue Cross—1935
460. English
461. Eight (McQuaid, Hickey, O'Hearn, Mooney, Kearney, Sheen, Hogan and Clark)
462. Clarissa Street Bridge
463. Susan B. Anthony
464. He was the first to fly over the city in a homemade aircraft.
465. Through Death Valley
466. Prostitution
467. They were just ordained ministers of the Universal Life Church; they claimed their homes were, therefore, tax-exempt.
468. Charlotte
469. Our Lady of Mercy High School
470. A urine sample
471. Coats
472. Lusitania
473. Prohibition
474. World War I food shortages
475. He had taken his own life.
476. Scrap metal was needed for the war effort.
477. Deaths
478. A structure fire
479. Frederick Douglass
480. A car
481. Fire hydrants
482. Richard M. Nixon
483. Rochesterville
484. On Charlotte's beaches
485. The medical effects of prolonged radiation exposure
486. Red-tailed hawks
487. Freedom, Independence, God, Honor, Today; originally, Integration
488. The Van Lare Sewage Treatment Plant "odor hotline"
489. Pearl Harbor
490. Her baby
491. To teach English
492. The Underground Railroad

HISTORY ANSWERS

493. The first suicide off the Veterans Memorial Bridge
494. Telephone line
495. Fight in the Civil War
496. German
497. Foot patrolmen
498. Main Street Bridge
499. Slavery
500. No
501. Razor blades (scrap metal)
502. Africa
503. Taverns; he supported temperance.
504. Drug addiction
505. Lakeshore Nursing Home
506. Discover a comet
507. Charles Lindbergh
508. A wing from atop the Times Square Building
509. Kate Gleason
510. Lake Ontario, in 1975; the idea—a landfill dike to catch Genesee River pollution
511. Presbyterians
512. Thick mud caused by the rain may have cushioned the impact.
513. Owing money
514. The "accident" at RG&E's Ginna plant
515. Nathaniel Rochester
516. No; he did visit twice during the 1960 campaign, though.
517. None
518. Herbert Lehman and Franklin Roosevelt
519. Social Security
520. Temperance
521. No body was ever found
522. Seth Green (Drive)
523. Whale oil
524. Our Mother of Sorrows in Greece
525. German
526. Contact visits—1980
527. Pilot error; the FAA said he landed the plane too fast.
528. Ontario Beach Park
529. Bought war bonds
530. It was destroyed by the village's first fire.
531. Replicas of the Nina, the Pinta and the Santa Maria
532. Pigs
533. Hitler's march through Austria
534. They were built with cobblestones.
535. Genesee Beer
536. Nathaniel Rochester
537. The Erie Canal through downtown Rochester

HISTORY ANSWERS

538. LaSalle
539. Bishop Kearney Marching Band
540. Anti-Mason Party
541. Four and a half gallons
542. A gym
543. Bicyclists
544. The city jail
545. Urban League and Action for a Better Community
546. First
547. The slot machine
548. They consumed a keg of rum.
549. Lewis Henry Morgan
550. Lilac bushes
551. Sex discrimination; there were no co-eds on campus.
552. The invasion of Cambodia by US troops
553. Victims of the "Double Initial" murders
554. Antietam
555. Kodak
556. Oswego or Sodus
557. Police directing traffic from pedestals in the middle of intersections
558. They could crack joints of their big toes audibly.
559. Mexico, known as "Spanish money"
560. He would have to cut it to test it.
561. Inside the Thurston Road Security Trust Bank, ending a day long hostage incident
562. Frederick Douglass
563. The A-Bomb test at Bikini Atoll
564. The Aqueduct
565. St. Luke's Episcopal
566. Police arrested a youth at a street dance.
567. Mutual aid
568. Steve May—1973
569. Monroe County unemployment
570. Republicans; she would be arrested for voting in that election anyway.
571. Barracks for German POWs
572. Italians
573. Ku Klux Klan
574. Children—11 and under
575. Pears
576. Prostitution
577. He was smuggling liquor from Canada during Prohibition.
578. $20—25,000
579. A military draft
580. Cholera
581. The 1975 crackdown on organized crime by County Sheriff's deputies

HISTORY ANSWERS

582. Bride
583. Carthage
584. Boats, trains and automobiles
585. Erie Canal
586. Women wouldn't be permitted to attend for 20 more years.
587. A Liberty Pole
588. Breaking rocks for pavement
589. The Seven Corners
590. A Canadian power surge
591. Pioneer ancestors in Rochester
592. Religious persecution by the French who wanted them to be Catholics
593. 30,000 union workers walked off their jobs because the city wouldn't let garbagemen unionize. "The Rochester General Strike" gained national attention. After one day, the city relented.
594. Frederick Douglass Building
595. First to build a house on land purchased from him
596. New York Governor DeWitt Clinton
597. The headline read "Red Light District No More!"
598. A prison (The Western House of Correction)
599. The demands were met.
600. The City of Rochester

GEOGRAPHY

601. On a 17th century European map of the world, this would have been the only visible landmark that would one day be part of Monroe County.

602. This was originally called "Woods of West Town," until 1818.

603. It caused the flooding of Lake Ontario's north shore in 1972.

604. How many waterfalls are created by the Genesee River in Monroe County?

605. Hundred Acre, Quaker, and Deep ponds are found in which county park?

606. In 1790, the land in this town north of Ridge Road was known by settlers as "The Black Forest" because trees grew so thick that little sun could filter through.

607. The Genesee is one of only two major rivers in the world that flow south to north. Name the other.

608. Over the years, there have been several attempts, all unsuccessful, to re-name this city street "Eastman Avenue."

609. Why was University Avenue so named?

610. How many Barge Canal locks does the state operate in Monroe County?

611. As Monroe Avenue, Rt. 31, moves through the village of Pittsford, what does it become?

612. What's the county's least densely populated village?

613. What town has the county's largest population?

614. One of Rochester's central downtown streets, it was originally called "Sophia Street" by Nathaniel Rochester, in honor of his wife.

615. Where is Windsor Beach?

616. The town of Pittsford was named after the hometown of local war hero Caleb Hopkins. "His" Pittsford was in which colonial state?

617. Corinthian Street once ran south from Main Street, across Court to Monroe Avenue. But it was obliterated with the construction of this building in the early 60's.

618. Of the five Great Lakes, where does Ontario rank in terms of size?

619. Over the years, this still-elegant city street has borne the names River Road, Blossom Road, Pittsford Street, and even Main Street!

620. In 1967, New York State announced plans to build a new east-west bridge over the Genesee because this one had become increasingly inadequate.

GEOGRAPHY

621. Rochester pioneers in July of 1810 awoke to find much of their vegetable crop severely damaged. What was the cause?

622. This town's name is shared with at least 30 other towns, counties, and villages across America.

623. It began on February 28th, 1900, and didn't end until March 2nd—63 hours later.

624. In 1901, Rochester was said to have the lowest mortality rate of any U.S. city. A University of Rochester geologist, Herman Fairchild, attributed this to what primary cause?

625. Before the Keeler Street Expressway, how did the Veterans Bridge outlet, St. Paul Boulevard, and Ridge Road East converge?

626. Early French Jesuits called it "Casconchiagon" in the 1750's.

627. Oliver Culver was the first supervisor of this town, though the road named after him does not enter or pass through it.

628. It is the official name of the bridge connecting Mt. Hope Avenue with Exchange Boulevard.

629. It's the only road in Monroe County with access ramps both ways to I-490 and 590.

630. It is, at its center, 500 feet above sea level.

631. What is the official name for the triangle of land on which the Liberty Pole is located?

632. It's not a village or a town, but still, developer Joseph Tone gave it a name in 1872 when he built "Tone's Summer Village of Homes."

633. It is the highest geographical point within the city limits.

634. This wiped out hundreds of trees that once lined exclusive East Avenue.

635. What were the hottest and coldest temperatures ever officially recorded in the city of Rochester?

636. The land that is now Rochester was purchased by three men: Rochester, Carroll, and this man, who is remembered in a downtown street name.

637. In a year, we see the sun shining in Rochester what per cent of its possible time?

638. Which of these had or were at one time considered sites for landfills: Holley, Riga, Rush, Caledonia, LeRoy, Penfield?

639. Why does the city salt, not sand icy roads?

640. The earliest Indians called it "Skanadario," or "very pretty one," according to tradition.

641. What county town has the smallest population?

642. On January 26, 1978, Rochester businesses shut down at noon, and stores were clogged with customers stocking up. Too, there was fear of a power failure. What caused the panic?

643. Before its cemetery opened, Mt. Hope Avenue, the extension of St. Paul Street and South Avenue, had another name. What was it?

644. What town is thought to be named after a city and province of Italy?

645. Which end of the Irondequoit Bay Bridge, Webster or Irondequoit, has the higher elevation?

646. What street is the official mailing address of City Hall?

647. This village became a "co-terminus" town, winning its independence in November of 1979.

648. By 1910, with roads a montage of trolleys, horses, and the new motor cars, this Rochester road became known as "Alley of Death."

649. The French explorers set up a fur trading post in 1717, calling it Fort Des Sables. Today you can find a "jack rabbit," but little other fur there. What do we call it?

650. Main Street was first called this. In later years it made sense because it headed in the direction of that city.

651. A newspaper contest to re-name this sparked 400 entries in the early 70's. The winning name was "The Eastern Cross-way," but we still prefer to call it by this other name.

652. What do the Rochester Plaza Hotel, the City Fire Academy, and the Riverside Cemetery have in common?

653. In the 1980's, the city unveiled an urban renewal project designed to upgrade this street. The street and the project were both named "La Avenida," the name used by Rochester's Ibero-Americans. What is this street known as?

654. If all the miles of road operated and owned by the City of Rochester were stretched end-to-end along the Thruway, would they reach New York City?

655. It was the city of Rochester's first public park, a gift from famed nurserymen Ellwanger and Barry.

656. In the 1970's, it was planned to be a city of 35,000, with three lakes, its own railroad, and 578 acres of business and industry.

657. In 1983, some 285 kinds were seen in Monroe County.

658. What formed the hills of Pinnacle and Cobbs?

659. In the 1830's, the section of the city populated with Irish immigrants was given a nickname. What was it?

660. When Hamlet Scrantom came to build the first real home along the Genesee in 1812, he encountered a foot of snow on the ground. What month was it?

661. Launched in 1976, the ESLO Fishing Derby has become America's largest. What does ESLO stand for?

662. Which creek empties into the Genesee farther downstream, Black or Oatka?

663. The Village of Fairport is part of what town?

664. What beach encloses Braddocks Bay?

665. A southeast city neighborhood is often referred to as the "white pants ghetto" because of its proximity to this building.

666. Where did the town of Hamlin get its name?

667. Despite its sound, this street was not named after royalty, but rather, a horse on Azariah Booty's farm.

668. A stone's throw from the Four Corners, it's officially called the Major Charles Carroll Plaza, in honor of one of Rochester's first land owners. What's it commonly known as?

669. This town was known, at various times, as Northfield, Boyle, and Smallwood.

670. Which is the largest of the ponds along Edgemere Drive?

671. Which of these cities gets more average yearly sunshine than Rochester: Denver, Chicago, or Minneapolis?

672. Although the site of the Liberty Pole is landscaped with rocks, this is the official name of the site.

673. Of Rochester's bridges across the Genesee, this one is the highest above water level.

674. True or False? Rochester's drinking water is fluoridated.

675. In which direction does water flow through Lake Ontario?

676. This land was a part of Greece from 1890 until it was annexed by the City of Rochester in 1918.

677. It's the largest village in Monroe County.

678. Over the years, this city neighborhood has been home to Germans, Irish, and Italians, but it never actually had a large population of the people after whom it is named. Name this west side area.

679. The river campus of the University of Rochester was once the site of a Rochester country club. Which one?

680. In which village can you find the county's largest Irish population?

681. It was the second worst snowstorm in Rochester history, dumping nearly 3 feet of snow, and shutting down everything for nearly 5 days. What was it called?

682. When Genesee Street, Rt. 383, leaves the city, what does it become?

683. This park contains America's oldest antique carousel.

684. In the pioneer days, this plot of land was known as "Rattlesnake Hill." One of Rochester's larger municipal buildings now rests atop it. Which one?

685. Which village has the largest percentage of its population 65 years old, and older?

686. Early Indians developed two paths that cut across Monroe County. One went east-west, connecting Indian villages. The north-south route led to the lake and the enemy French troops. In English, what were these two paths called?

687. This causes it to snow more in Irondequoit than in Brighton.

688. Black Creek flows through this Monroe County village.

689. In the summer of 1975, several cars and hapless pedestrians dropped through gaping holes downtown. What caused this terra-non-firma incident?

690. Through the 1940's, glass-eating Herbert "Paddy" Padock, head of the Rochester tank of Hoboes of America, was regarded as the "mayor" of this downtown street.

691. His works included *A River Ramble* and *Slim Fingers Beckon*, inside looks at the area's geographical history.

692. It was originally named "Hogback Road." By 1913, it was re-named as part of a city road extension, and its name now bears tribute to a high school on the block.

693. In the pioneer days, Buffalo and Mill Streets intersected to form an area that still bears its pioneer nickname. What is it?

694. It's the nickname given to the steepest hill in Durand-Eastman Park, where only the bravest of sledders give it a go in the winter.

695. This neighborhood got its name from the practice of residents who kept pigs in their yards.

696. This major north-south road was named after Rochester's first shipbuilder, and fittingly enough, follow it north and it leads to the Lake Ontario shoreline.

697. In 1786, it was known as Montgomery, and by 1789, it was subdivided and known as Ontario. By 1821, it was smaller still, and known by still another name.

698. In 1859, East Main Street was known simply as "Main Street." What was West Main Street called?

699. True or False? Irondequoit Bay was once completely open to Lake Ontario, with British and French exploring ships sailing freely into it.

700. The Indians called this "Ontario Trail" because its route followed the receding edge of the Great Lake.

GEOGRAPHY

701. What is the name for the strip of land between Lake Ontario and Buck Pond in Greece?

702. Which town grew more from 1960 to 1980, Brighton or Gates?

703. It's the official name of the Route 104 expressway.

704. The Little Massaug and Big Massaug coves are visible from what bridge?

705. Allens Creek in Brighton empties into these larger waters.

706. At 981 feet, it's the longest bridge across the Genesee in Monroe County.

707. Where would you find the following streets: Adlington Avenue, Indian Trail Avenue, Firemans Avenue, and Green Tree Avenue? It's a neighborhood almost as old as the city itself.

708. By 1900 it was referred to as "the village with six churches and six saloons."

709. This town's motto is "Where Life Is Worth Living."

710. The Marketview Heights neighborhood is the namesake of this city attraction located in its center.

711. Its base is tilting to the south 20 centimeters every century.

712. Though on a much smaller scale, this downtown roadway was first proposed nearly 70 years ago by Mayor Hiram Edgerton.

713. As the Thruway enters Monroe County from the east, what's the first road that passes over it.?

714. At 200 miles, it is the longest street in New York State, highways excluded.

715. This town's name is translated to mean "where the waves gasp and die."

716. This lakeside neighborhood derived its nickname from the tents that its residents used to put up over wood frames at the start of each summer season.

717. All built in the 1920's, there are four roads or dugways that cut across the Irondequoit valley from west to east. Name them.

718. In 1853, this was the last town to join Monroe County.

719. In the late 1880's, something was missing from Cobbs and Pinnacle hills that is present today. What wasn't there?

720. In Monroe County, three "port" cities all sprang up as a result of the Erie Canal. Name them.

721. In what town is Irondequoit Bay Park East?

722. What's the name of the road that forms the western border of the University of Rochester campus along the Genesee?

723. In 1977, there was a short-lived movement in the black community to re-name Jefferson Avenue. What would the street have been called?

724. In Rochester's first days, settlers often reported seeing huge flocks of birds that would "cloud out the sun," and they organized hunts to thin out the population. Name the bird.

725. The need to transport supplies to Fort Niagara during the War of 1812 was the major reason for the upgrading of this road.

726. There are 422,310 of these in Monroe County.

727. Monroe County "lost" 33,000 residents in the summer of 1980. How?

728. By 1975, Gloria Drive had become synonymous with what ecological phenomenon?

729. Traveling southbound on South Avenue past Court, if you bear to your left, you'll get on the ramp to 490 East. Straight ahead is South Avenue. What will happen if you bear far right?

730. Four parks line the Genesee in Monroe County. Name them.

731. Which is closer to Rochester, Watertown or Toronto?

732. Rochester has 7 sister cities: Rennes, Caltinisetta, Rehovot, Bamako, Waterford, Wurzburg, and Krakow. Which is farthest from the Four Corners?

733. When this road was constructed over the Erie Canal bed, suggested names included Towpath Avenue, Erie Boulevard, and Aldridge Concourse (in honor of the GOP boss). What was the much less creative name chosen instead?

734. In 1972, a Cleveland firm proposed a complex of 6 twenty-three-story high-rises that would have housed 10,000 people in the shadow of Aquinas Stadium. What was this planned community going to be called?

735. In 1788, Phelps and Gorham purchased 6.25 million acres that would include most of the land from Geneva to the east bank of the Genesee. What was the price per acre?

736. There are actually two reservoirs in the city of Rochester. One at Cobbs Hill. But where's the other?

737. After a mail-in contest in the 60's, "A Town of Friendship" was the epithet selected for this town.

738. Is it possible to hear the Ginna nuclear warning sirens from Panorama Plaza in Penfield?

739. According to the 1980 census, it takes commuters from this county town the longest to reach downtown.

740. In 1928, the heads of RG&E and Rochester Tel proposed a plan to simplify the names given to Rochester streets. What was their plan?

GEOGRAPHY

741. In a 1932 zoning dispute, Harper Sibley said of this street, "It's the finest residential street in America and we intend to keep it so." What was the street?

742. In 1797, there were only four post offices in western New York. They were located in Bath, Geneva, Williamsburg, and in this place, the closest to what is now Rochester. Name the city.

743. On the Route 15 approach to Rochester, the city skyline first becomes visible from its peak.

744. Which is the county's most densely populated town?

745. In 1979, it had the highest median family income, at $36,000.

746. Where in the county can Lake Lacomo and Lily Pond be found?

747. This mile-long city street got its name from the traders who used it heading north from Canandaigua, through the city, toward what is now Irondequoit and the Genesee River, a 30-mile route.

748. The city of Rochester has a street named after every Ivy League college but one. Name it.

749. Located on the south side of the Erie Canal, "Rotten Row" was downtown's first slum, filled with drunks and vagrants. What business building now occupies the land of "Rotten Row"?

750. What lake is totally contained *within* the city limits?

751. The linden is the official one for the city of Rochester; it's distinguished by its yellowish-white coloring.

752. On July 1, 1932, one hundred Saratoga Avenue shade trees, a 300-foot Dewey Avenue warehouse, and a good deal of Jones Park were destroyed. What was the cause?

753. A major downtown street was originally named after Charles Carroll, one of the men who journeyed north with Nathaniel Rochester. But the city council had a falling out with his family, and re-named it. What was the new name?

754. Originally called Exposition Park, its name was changed to honor this man's 14 years as Rochester mayor.

755. This city neighborhood got its name from the daughter of one of the county's first land agents.

756. How many bridges (including expressway crossovers) span the Genesee River within the city of Rochester?

757. This road near Summerville got its name from the large granite boulders the railroad brought in to protect its tracks from Lake Ontario waters.

758. In Iroquois, this village name means "finger on the ground."

759. Salmon Creek in Greece flows into this bay.

760. From where does the town of Penfield derive its name?

761. Where in Monroe County can you find the minerals epidote, magnetite, hornblende, corundum, and zircon?

762. Two huge lakes, since named Warren and Iroquois, once covered large land areas to the south and east of Lake Ontario. What happened to them?

763. When neighborhood factions came up with no name that they could agree upon for this street, the city engineer decided for them. What was the northeast street named?

764. What is the name for the sandbar, turned beach, that closes off the mouth of Irondequoit Bay from Lake Ontario?

765. Acquired in 1928, this 1,650 acres is Monroe County's largest park.

766. In what town does the Genesee River begin?

767. A blasting powder plant was the inspiration for the name of this county park.

768. Of this phenomenon, a turn-of-the-century Chamber of Commerce pamphlet wrote, "They are of health-giving nature and such as to conduce the well-being of hardy, hustling people."

769. In 1976, U of R research scientist David Dutton disproved the myth of Spook Hill, near Canandaigua Lake, that had fascinated Rochesterians for years. What was the myth?

770. On the average, Rochester has "thunderstorm days" that total how many days out of the year?

771. Which town has the highest percentage of teenagers in its population?

772. What town's population exploded by 184% in the decade of the 1960's?

773. Although it's fairly common on other lakes, it happened for the first time on Ontario, February 9, 1934.

774. Nathaniel Rochester was born in the same Virginia county and grew up with two United States presidents. He would use their names for two locations here in Genesee country. Who were they?

775. Pont de Rennes is a pedestrian bridge overlooking the Genesee. What did it used to be called?

776. Which town in Monroe County has the most educated population?

777. Why was Basket Road in Webster so named?

778. The first organized church in Monroe County was begun in this town.

779. By 1838, Rochester had been divided into 5 wards. The Second and Fifth lined the Genesee to the north of Main Street. The Third and Fourth lined the Genesee to the south. Where was the First Ward?

780. In the summer of '72, dirt dikes were built along River Road to prevent flooding of the RIT campus and riverbank homes. It was thought that the Mount Morris Dam might overflow, for the first time in its history. What was the cause?

781. On the average, in a year, Rochester has this many days when temperatures top 90 degrees.

782. Which comes closest to the number of miles of lake shoreline there are in Monroe County: 25, 35, 45, or 55?

783. Geologist Herman Fairchild wrote that this was ". . . the cause, explanation or apology for the city of Rochester." What was it?

784. This town has the county's smallest percentage of blacks.

785. What is the name of the bridge that connects Lyell Avenue, on the west, to St. Paul Street, on the east?

786. In the 50's, urban renewal projects built two housing units on the city's northeast side; one for low-income families was called Hanover Houses. What was the name of the project for middle-income families?

787. A $185,000 street repair project straightened this aptly named stretch of road on Beach Avenue in Charlotte.

788. If you started at I-90 in Henrietta and traveled westbound as far as the road would go, where would you be?

789. What buildings anchor downtown's Four Corners?

790. When it was formed, East Rochester originally went by another name. What was it?

791. This municipal park is noted for its extensive exhibit of roses.

792. What county borders Monroe to the northeast?

793. There is still a name in city geography that bears witness to a range of hills that cut across from the Genesee to Highland and Cobbs Hill parks. What was that range called?

794. From this spot on the Genesee in Rochester, it is possible to see shale rock formations nearly 500 million years old.

795. Before its original site on Prince Street, a west side location was planned for the U of R. A road, College Avenue, was even mapped out. That neighborhood that would have been a college campus still exists. Name it.

796. The town of Greece was named after the country. How come?

797. This town was originally named Inverness, in honor of the many Scottish settlers who lived there as grain farmers.

798. Through Rochester's recorded weather history, these ten days in a row are traditionally the coldest.

799. To this day, it still raises the pollution levels that close the beach at Charlotte.

800. There used to be several, but now this is the only lift bridge over the Genesee in Monroe County.

GEOGRAPHY

801. This town found its name in South America, with a slight alteration.

802. In the 1960's, Monroe County was known by another name, according to WOKR-TV. What was that name?

803. The lilac shrub is indigenous to this place, and is thought to have originated there.

804. True or False? Lake Ontario is the deepest of the Great Lakes.

805. Heading southbound on 590 into the "Can," if you bore to your left, what would be your first available exit?

806. Before the installation of a sewer system, what did Rochester do with its raw sewage?

807. At the turn of the 18th century, this town was purchased for 36 cents an acre.

808. Before the Ice Age, the Genesee River took a much different route through Monroe County. A waterway still bears witness to that route. What is it?

809. What streets intersect to form the Twelve Corners?

810. In what park would you find Zoo and Horseshoe roads?

811. During the first 10 days of May, as many as 10,000 a day may pass through Braddock Bay Park.

812. In 1801, these four were in the area that is now Monroe County: Northampton, Northfield, Hartford, and Bloomfield. What were they?

813. Which of the Finger Lakes is closest to Rochester, due south?

814. It's the reason often given for why more expensive suburbs tend to spring up on the *east* side of a city such as Rochester.

815. When Empire Boulevard (Rt. 404) heads east toward Webster, what road does it become?

816. Some of the Indians that began inhabiting the Genesee valley around 1300 are believed to have migrated here from lands that now make up which bordering state?

817. An early 1800's plan to open a Rochester stockyard was never carried out. Nevertheless, this earmarked area still bears the name of the tavern built and aptly named, in anticipation of the stockyard.

818. True or false? Adjusting the flow in the St. Lawrence Seaway affects the level of Lake Ontario because more Atlantic Ocean water is let in.

819. Had a 1926 court decision gone the other way, Ontario Beach would have become part of another state. Which one?

820. The foghorn tower at Ontario Beach is located on which side of the Genesee River mouth, east or west?

GEOGRAPHY

821. Where would you find Snyder Island?

822. Until the 20th century, the largest field of wheat ever harvested by machine was located in this town.

823. The French explorers called it Frontenac Lake. We have another name for it today.

824. Where's the bull's head at Bull's Head?

825. Besides the night club, is there really a Red Creek?

826. Several paintings of this Genesee Country thoroughfare hang in the Smithsonian Institute. Painted by Rochester artist Irwin Porter, what is the subject of the works?

827. Its town seal bears the word "Gerundegut."

828. To the nearest foot, how much snow fell during the five days of the Blizzard of '66?

829. If you started out on Route 96 in Bushnell's Basin, and traveled northwest as far as the route would take you, at what landmark would you end up?

830 True or false? The Rochester metropolitan area population declined between censuses in 1970 and 1980.

GEOGRAPHY

831. In the pioneer days, wild settlers labeled "Turks" inhabited a highland area in the southeast corner of what is now Monroe County. A street now memorializes this spot. Name it.

832. This 1,500-acre planned community has its own public school, swimming pool, and lakes.

833. Which expressway travels through Greece: 390, 490, or 590?

834. This giant of American literature once said, "Rochester is noted for having a neighboring village CHARlotte, that the natives insist on calling shaLOT."

835. In the original plan, this city street was to be converted into the beginning of the Eastern Expressway (490 on the city's east side).

836. Where does the city put the snow that plows and trucks have cleared from city streets?

837. This village grew up around the water used to drive Norton's Mill, which was the village's original name. What is it today?

838. Where in Monroe County would you find kames, eskers, and kettles?

839. In terms of population, how does Rochester rank in the state?

840. How many acres of Genesee Valley Park were destroyed to make way for the 1.08-mile stretch of the Outer Loop?

841. What town has the largest Italian population?

842. It's actually only 680 acres, but the Thousand Acre Swamp can be found in this Monroe County town.

843. There's a city neighborhood north of Holleder Stadium that has a decidedly "county" flavor to it, because of seven of its streets. How come?

844. Over the years it's gone by various names: the Lewiston Road, The Alluvial Way, and The Honeymoon Trail, among them.

845. Which town has the most air conditioners in single-family homes?

846. In 1836, city surveyor Silas Cornell wanted to name it "Mount Auburn."

847. By standing in one spot at this location, you can see Kodak Tower, the Sibley building, the statue of Mercury, and all four seasons, with a railroad to boot!

848. In 1638, it was part of "Terra Incognita," a term bestowed by the Dutch government.

849. In the 1890's, a section of Exchange Street was dubbed "Murderer's Row." What type of area was it?

850. The Seneca Indians named it and told Jacques Cartier of its existence in 1534. The name meant "pleasant banks."

851. When Elmwood Avenue crosses East Avenue, the road name changes. What does it become?

852. Called the most important place in the early history of Genesee Country, Indian's Landing was the gateway to the south, with many passing through during the French and Indian and the 1812 wars. Between what two roads can you find this site today?

853. Between 1970 and 1980, this is the only county town whose population dropped.

854. What town population has the greatest number of people who were born outside of New York State?

855. For the first recorded time, they froze on January 6, 1827.

856. What town is named after the Countess of Bath, daughter of Sir William Pultney?

857. "It's like going straight into Hell itself!" That's how Bezaleel Atchinson's wife, Polly, described the land that would become this county town. They stayed to become its first settlers.

858. How did Turning Point Park get its name?

859. If you stood at the Four Corners site in the year 8,000 B.C., what would you be seeing?

860. Where is Cornerstone Park?

GEOGRAPHY

861. What city street cuts through more ZIP codes, Alexander Street or Hudson Avenue?

862. It's been dubbed "Mooney's Mountain" and "The Left Bank." Where can this man-made drumlin be found?

863. The first schoolhouse in the county, Number One Mile Post School, was erected in this town.

864. In 1797, the lost city of Tryon sprung up with its own grist mill and flour shipping docks. But it wasn't on the Genesee. What body of water did it utilize, instead?

865. How many miles long is the Genesee River, to the nearest ten?

866. This city neighborhood gets its name from its ZIP code. What's it called?

867. Running along the Genesee, it was known both as Mason Street and Market Street, but dubbed "the Bowery of Western New York." Now it's a memory. What was the street's final name?

868. Oatka Creek flows through which Monroe County village?

869. How many Finger Lakes are there?

870. When Westfall Road heads north across Monroe Avenue, the name of the road changes. What does it become?

871. The old aqueduct across the Genesee is now covered by this.

872. The Jewish Community Center is located in this town.

873. In what body of water was one likely to find packet boats in the 19th century?

874. Throughout history, this Monroe County village also has been known as Salmon Creek, Tyler's Corners, and North Parma.

875. The Third Ward once carried this nickname, tribute to the "upper crust" who lived there.

876. It's the name given to the predominantly black neighborhood in the Third Ward, bordered by Genesee, Bronson, VanAuker, and West Main.

877. There's a spot along Irondequoit Bay to this day known as "Birds and Worms." The name was derived from two outdoorsmen clubs. What did the members do?

878. Which town had the largest percentage growth from 1970 to 1980?

879. What was Council Rock, in Brighton?

880. With the boom of the 60's, there were plans on the boards to build a highway connecting Irondequoit Bay in a wide arc with Scottsville and the Thruway, outside the Outer Loop. What was this roadway going to be called?

881. In most stretches now, it's a four-lane, east-west county road, but in 1700 it was the Indians' main thoroughfare: just a foot-wide path!

882. Monroe County's first library was organized on Ezra Patterson's farm. Subscribers paid $1 to become members in 1803. In what town was the farm located?

883. This downtown street was named in honor of the man who helped bring the Erie Canal to Rochester.

884. This building is depicted on the seal of the Town of Greece.

885. How many feet wide is Main Street downtown?

GEOGRAPHY ANSWERS

601. Irondequoit Bay
602. Henrietta
603. Hurricane Agnes
604. Two; the Upper and Lower. The Court St. Dam "falls" don't count.
605. Mendon Ponds Park
606. Greece
607. The Nile
608. Main Street
609. It bordered the original U of R campus on Prince Street.
610. Two; #32 at Clover St. and #33 at Edgewood
611. Pittsford-Palmyra Road
612. Honeoye Falls
613. Greece; 81,367
614. Plymouth Avenue
615. At the mouth of the Genesee
616. Vermont
617. Midtown Plaza
618. Fifth; it's the smallest.
619. East Avenue
620. Stutson Street Bridge
621. Severe frost
622. Webster
623. Rochester's biggest snowstorm (43.1″)
624. Lake Ontario, which he said moderated temperature changes
625. In a traffic circle
626. Genesee River
627. Brighton
628. Ford Street Bridge; Council changed the name from "Clarissa" in 1977
629. Monroe Avenue
630. Rochester
631. John F. Kennedy Square
632. Summerville
633. Pinnacle Hill
634. Dutch elm disease
635. -22° Feb. 9, 1934; +102° July 9-10, 1936
636. Fitzhugh
637. 54%
638. They all were!
639. Sand clogs sewers.
640. Lake Ontario
641. Rush; 3,001
642. A predicted snow storm that never materialized
643. South St. Paul Street
644. Parma

GEOGRAPHY ANSWERS

645. It's 15 feet higher by the time it reaches Webster.
646. Church Street
647. East Rochester
648. Main Street
649. Sea Breeze
650. Buffalo Street
651. Can of Worms
652. The west bank of the Genesee
653. Clinton Avenue North
654. Yes and then some; the city owns 538 miles of road.
655. Highland
656. Riverton
657. Birds
658. A 10,000-year-old glacier
659. Dublin
660. May; he should have taken the hint and moved on.
661. Empire State—Lake Ontario
662. Black Creek
663. Perinton
664. Manitou Beach
665. Strong Memorial Hospital
666. Hannibal Hamlin, Lincoln's first vice-president in 1861
667. Prince Street
668. Crossroads Park, behind the Rochester Plaza and Federal Building
669. Brighton
670. Long Pond
671. All of them
672. Liberty Pole Green
673. Driving Park Bridge; 200 feet up
674. True
675. West to east
676. Kodak Park
677. Brockport
678. Dutchtown; the name is actually an Americanization of "Deutsche," meaning German.
679. Oak Hill
680. Brockport; 745
681. The Blizzard of '66
682. Scottsville Road
683. Ontario Beach Park
684. Monroe County Office Building
685. Pittsford; 17.9%
686. Path of Peace and Warpath
687. Lake Ontario (lake effect snows)
688. Churchville
689. Underground subway caverns beneath downtown streets

GEOGRAPHY ANSWERS

690. Front Street
691. Arch Merrill
692. Kings Highway
693. The Four Corners
694. Suicide Hill
695. Swillburg
696. (Oliver) Culver Road
697. Monroe County
698. West Avenue
699. True
700. Ridge Road
701. Crescent Beach
702. Gates
703. The Keeler Street Expressway
704. Irondequoit Bay Bridge
705. Irondequoit Creek
706. Veterans' Memorial Bridge
707. Mount Hope Cemetery
708. Pittsford
709. Webster
710. Public Market
711. Lake Ontario
712. The Inner Loop
713. Route 64; Mendon Road
714. Route 104 (Ridge Road)
715. Irondequoit
716. White City
717. Atlantic Avenue, Blossom Road, Empire Blvd., Penfield Road
718. Hamlin
719. Trees; they had all been chopped down for building lumber.
720. Fairport, Spencerport and Brockport
721. Penfield
722. Joseph C. Wilson Boulevard; formerly River Blvd.—renamed 1971
723. Dr. Martin Luther King Drive
724. Pigeon
725. Ridge Road
726. Acres
727. Census Bureau error
728. The landfill
729. You'll still be getting on 490 East; there are 2 access ramps.
730. Genesee Valley, Maplewood, Seneca and Turning Point
731. Watertown—130 miles (Toronto—170)
732. Rehovot, Israel—5,800 miles

GEOGRAPHY ANSWERS

733. Broad Street
734. Stadium City
735. Three cents
736. Highland Park
737. Henrietta
738. No, that's outside the ten-mile audible radius
739. Hamlin, 28.9 minutes
740. Number them all like Manhattan; without a similar grid pattern, though, the plan was quickly shelved.
741. East Avenue
742. Canandaigua
743. Methodist Hill in Henrietta
744. Irondequoit
745. Pittsford
746. Powder Mill Park (Bushnell's Basin)
747. Merchants Road
748. Yale
749. The Gannett newspaper building
750. Lake Riley in Cobbs Hill Park (at 490 and Culver Road)
751. Tree; proclaimed in 1984
752. Monroe County's only recorded tornado
753. State Street
754. (Hiram) Edgerton Park
755. Charlotte
756. Thirteen
757. Rock Beach Road
758. Honeoye (Falls)
759. Braddock Bay
760. One of its first settlers, Daniel Penfield
761. On the beaches of Lake Ontario
762. They were formed by a huge glacier that backed up streams; as the glacier melted, the streams began to flow again.
763. Emanon Street ("No Name" backwards)
764. Oklahoma Beach
765. Mendon Ponds Park
766. Gold, Pennsylvania
767. Powder Mill Park
768. Rochester winters
769. Things rolled uphill; Dutton proved it an optical illusion.
770. 29
771. Rush; 27.8%
772. Henrietta
773. The lake froze from shore to shore.
774. Washington (Street) and Monroe (County)
775. Platt Street Bridge
776. Brighton; 44% over 25 have college degrees.

GEOGRAPHY ANSWERS

777. People along it made baskets for Webster's fruit crop.
778. Penfield
779. The Four Corners
780. Hurricane Agnes' torrential rains
781. Two
782. 35
783. Genesee River
784. Mendon; 0.2%
785. Bausch Memorial Bridge
786. Chatham Gardens
787. Dead Man's Curve
788. Seattle, Washington
789. Powers, Crossroads, Wilder and Four Corners buildings
790. Despatch, named after the railroad car company located there
791. Maplewood
792. Wayne
793. Pinnacle Range
794. Genesee River Gorge at Driving Park
795. Bull's Head
796. It had just won its independence from Turkey when the town formed.
797. Wheatland
798. February 1-10
799. Heavy rain backs up city sewers into the Genesee River.
800. Stutson Street
801. Chili
802. "13 Country"
803. Persia
804. False; Lake Superior is.
805. Linden Avenue; it's illegal to cross the white traffic line and exit at Penfield Road.
806. Dumped it into the Genesee River
807. Pittsford
808. Irondequoit Creek
809. Winton Road, Elmwood Avenue and Monroe Avenue
810. Durand-Eastman Park
811. Hawks
812. Towns
813. Conesus
814. The sun will always be behind commuting motorists.
815. Ridge Road
816. Ohio
817. Bull's Head
818. False; with the flow west to east, Ontario water is backed up.
819. Massachusetts; the state went to court to settle a colonial land claim, but the court threw it out almost immediately.

GEOGRAPHY ANSWERS

820. West
821. Irondequoit Bay
822. Sweden
823. Lake Ontario
824. There's the bust of a bull atop 894 West Main Street.
825. Yes; it's the creek that flows through Genesee Valley Park.
826. Erie Canal
827. Irondequoit
828. Three feet (34 inches)
829. Liberty Pole
830. False; it actually grew 1.1%.
831. Turk Hill Road
832. Gananda
833. I-390
834. Mark Twain
835. University Avenue
836. Into the Genesee River
837. Honeoye Falls
838. Everywhere; they're all glacier formations of the landscape.
839. Third
840. Ten acres
841. Irondequoit; 12,929
842. Penfield
843. They're all named after county towns.
844. Ridge Road
845. Greece; 3,999
846. Mount Hope Cemetery
847. Edgerton Park Model Train Exhibit and Museum
848. Rochester, Monroe County . . . in fact, all of New York west of Albany was "land unknown."
849. A "red light district"
850. Genesee River
851. Linden Avenue
852. Atlantic Avenue and Blossom Road (in Ellison Park)
853. Irondequoit
854. Greece; 15,233
855. Genesee River's Lower Falls
856. Henrietta
857. Parma
858. It's bordering the spot in the Genesee where boats would turn around for the trip back to Canada.
859. A glacier, 6,000 feet tall, stretching out as far as you could see
860. Behind Rochester Telephone offices at Broad and Stone streets
861. Alexander Street (4)
862. Between lanes of 490-West, near Culver Road
863. Pittsford

GEOGRAPHY ANSWERS

864. Irondequoit Creek
865. 140 (144 miles)
866. 14621
867. Front Street
868. Scottsville
869. Eleven
870. Allens Creek Road
871. Broad Street Bridge
872. Technically it's Henrietta.
873. Erie Canal
874. Hilton
875. "Ruffled Shirt Ward"
876. Chocolate City
877. Fish and hunt
878. Hamlin; +84%
879. A traditional meeting place for Seneca Indians
880. The Outer-Outer Loop
881. Ridge Road
882. Pittsford
883. (DeWitt) Clinton Avenue
884. The *Charlotte* lighthouse, a town landmark before its annexation to the city
885. Approximately sixty feet

886. In 1920, the Duffy-Powers Dry Goods Store instituted the "latest thing" in grocery marketing. What was the innovation that drew crowds of curious shoppers?

887. In 1950, the 914 model was the first one.

888. They were first issued in 1887, stamped with large lettering and drawings of horses and horsecars.

889. On February 25, 1946, Chemical & Metallurgical Magazine cited two local industries for awards for their work on the Manhattan Project, the development of the first atomic bomb. Name the firms.

890. According to the advertisements, what would you be treated to if you shopped at "The Big 125" furniture store?

891. What are Knabes, Chickerings, and Mason-Hamlins?

892. Over the years, it was known as the Sagamore and the Sheraton. This hotel still does business from the same East Avenue address.

893. In 1865, Western Union magnate Hiram Sibley paid the highest recorded income tax in Rochester on his $103,000 in earnings. What per cent was his income tax?

894. It was known as the "English Plan" and adopted 3 years earlier in Boston. Rochester stores agreed in the summer of 1860, that for the benefit of customers who worked days, this would be their new closing time.

895. In 1970 and '71, he won back-to-back scoring and MVP titles in the NASL. A decade later, he would own and operate St. Paul Street and Main Street pizza parlors.

896. The flour used to make this bakery treat was first developed by 19th century Rochesterian Sylvester Graham.

897. Which shopping center has the most stores: Midtown Plaza, Longridge Mall, or Greece Town Mall?

898. Jehiel Barnard made it for Miller Francis Brown in 1812, from a piece of cloth purchased in Massachusetts.

899. It was Rochester's first confectionery factory, built in 1924, and named after the "mother of level measurement."

900. Throughout the 1970's, it was Rochester's leading retailer of African art, clothing, jewelry, and artifacts.

901. When his mammoth show elephant, Jumbo, met an untimely death, P.T. Barnum commissioned this local firm, still in business, to mount it.

902. On May 23, 1968, the City of Rochester got into the transportation business. How?

903. 65,000 Rochesterians marched in a 1933 downtown parade that lasted 7 hours and included 71 marching bands. What prompted the celebration?

904. This village saw the manufacture of the first 100 harvesters made in the world.

905. At the turn of the century, the city hired inspectors to check bottled milk. Some sellers were watering down their milk with this.

906. H.H. Warner of the Safe Liver Cure Pill Company was the first president of this august body of business leaders back in 1888.

907. Its longest strike lasted more than six months; its shortest, less than six hours.

908. The B. Forman store opened its first shop in Rochester on Clinton Avenue in 1911. What does the "B" stand for?

909. A by-product of clearing fields for wheat, it became the second biggest product of 1820 Genesee Country, second only to wheat.

910. In 1955, Rochester Community Baseball stock was offered at $10 a share. What's the quoted bid on a share of it today?

911. John Jacob Bausch used this material to make the first frame for spectacles.

912. In 1946, R.T. French Company branched out from mustard and spices, entering the convenience food market with this product.

913. The advertising for this local beverage featured a waitress in top hat and tails.

914. Until 1876, Rochester presses published only farm journals. In that year, the first trade publication was printed and distributed to undertakers across America. What was its title?

915. What do Desenex, Allerest, and Cruex all have in common?

916. He once said: "To make good goods requires experience and is a slow matter—perhaps slower with me than it might be with someone else, but I do the best I know how."

917. It was the first printed as a four-page supplement to the Democrat and Chronicle on a Sunday in March 1906.

918. How many stories are there in the Xerox Tower?

919. What does Sibley's have in common with nationally known department stores Lord & Taylor, Baer & Fuller, and Hengerers & Stix?

920. Harold Smith began his business in an Ormond Street store front. Thirty years later, his sauce and fat burgers have become Rochester gastronomic institutions. Name his restaurant.

921. While French's put Rochester on the mustard map, another local company had gained nationwide status with its Blue Label ketchup. Name it.

922. At the second Women's Rights Convention held in Rochester in 1848, a report found that most seamstresses were working 15-hour days. How much were they paid an hour?

923. Begun in 1937 amid steaming pots in the family kitchen, this business now employs over 300.

924. Once the major industry of The Flour City, this occupational category included 2,277 people here in 1980, according to the Census Bureau.

925. Five Rochester companies are among the Fortune 500. Everyone knows that Kodak, Xerox, and Bausch & Lomb are listed, but what are the other two?

926. Mr. William Sutton is credited as the first to develop this variety of fruit that, worldwide, still bears the name of its originating town.

927. Every Saturday in October, Jimmy's Restaurant at the Public Market is a popular breakfast spot for people of a certain calling. Who are they?

928. Pat and J. Paul Brennan were sued by Uncle Sam and routed out of business. What was their line of work?

929. Although it was made at home or imported long before 1855, that's when Jacob Rau began the first production of this in Rochester.

930. It's the only western New York college to offer a major in gerontology, the study of old age.

931. It's the county's oldest major outdoor shopping plaza.

932. In 1977, this local bank was the original sponsor of the women's pro golf tournament in Rochester.

933. In 1932, Rochesterians bought $32 million worth of these.

934. In 1980, the City of Rochester ran TV commercials for a "product" that would "give you more for less." What was this advertised bargain?

935. Eddie David began this diet-busting business baking them in his own kitchen.

936. It's believed that this Rochester product was first used nationally in this manner in 1928, at Scheib Park, home of the Philadelphia Athletics. Name the product.

937. The village of Fairport once grew mulberry trees with the expressed purpose of producing a quality clothing material. What was it?

938. The U.S. Government manufactured 845 million of these before stopping.

939. At one time, there were three of these open (discreetly) for business on South Clinton between Main and Court streets.

940. At the turn of the century, some French wineries made champagne from this export, grown in the fields of Irondequoit.

941. In the 50's, Wegmans shoppers could turn in a filled red stamp book for money off on their groceries. What was the cash value of the book?

942. By 1912, 1,500 Rochesterians, using processed vegetable ivory, produced one half of the world's supply. Of what?

943. At the turn of the century, Rochesterians could buy a "Selden," advertised as "a home product." What was it?

944. Unionized employees at Xerox belong to what labor organization?

945. Amos Cobb developed this process which still supports a major industry in Fairport.

946. At noon, what country is featured on Midtown's Clock of Nations?

947. It's believed that this Rochester product was named after Frank Brownell, who headed up the manufacturing plant where it was made.

948. In 1813, this Monroe Avenue furniture store was originally built, but known then as the Billinghurst Black Horse Tavern.

949. Near the turn of the century, many inventive bar owners in the city put stalls in their establishments. Who used them?

950. Notre Dame's Fighting Irish and the New Jersey Generals have something Rochesterian in common. Name it.

951. Name the aviation company operated by the Wilmots.

952. Which has more physicians per 100,000—Rochester, New York, or Rochester, Minnesota?

953. What caused the great Sibley's fire of 1904?

954. This high tech center was formerly known as the East Rochester Village Mall.

955. This sugary treat and the machinery to form its familiar shape were both developed right here in Rochester.

956. Kodak's Elmgove plant has an official company name. What is it?

957. At 20,000 square feet, located on Clinton Avenue South, it was the largest of its kind in New York State in 1930.

958. While they were neighbors on Humboldt Street, Stromberg-Carlson and WROC once had this in common.

959. Eastview Mall was originally planned to be constructed in what town inside Monroe County?

960. Today, there are more than two dozen countywide serving this cuisine. The first one opened in Rochester in 1907.

961. James Cutler's invention made it easier for everyone to "drop a line." What was it?

962. Rochester nurseryman James Vick introduced this new form of retailing in the 1860's.

963. This restaurant was named for the small creeks that flowed nearby, through the Oak Hill Country Club.

964. Not known for health products, this company manufactured the world's first synthetic vitamin A.

965. This town has the largest number of finance, real estate, and insurance agents.

966. What's a "hack plate"?

967. In 1895, several Rochester saloons changed their names so that they could legally sell liquor on Sundays. What did these saloons "become"?

968. Through the 50's and 60's, First Federal Bank jingles featured a character named "HWD," a coin with a head, arms, and legs. What was HWD?

969. Malcolm Gray, owner of the Gray Metal Company of Rochester, began this now widespread modern labor practice in January of 1922, to the delight of his workers.

970. As listed in the 1984 directory, which fast food chain has the most outlets countywide: Burger King, McDonald's, or Wendy's?

971. Abelard Reynolds was the first businessman to install these in downtown Rochester to lure shoppers off the streets and into his arcade.

972. This family-owned industry now deals in industrial textiles and weather seal insulation, but in the Gay Nineties, they made bindings for women's skirts.

973. In 1983, Strong Memorial Hospital estimated the cost at $4,000 to $6,000 per attempt.

974. Rochester's domination of the world export market ended when this industry finally boomed in Minneapolis.

975. It opened in February 1978, in the heart of downtown, and went out of business 23 months later.

976. In 1931, Colonial Western was the first to stop here on a run between New York City and Cleveland. What was the business?

977. Begun in 1981 with one Henrietta stand, Zab's is now a million dollar business. They use one word in their official name to describe their hot dogs. What's the word?

978. As the Depression deepened, this Rochester industry actually hired 900 workers, opening up a plant it had moved from Dayton, Ohio.

979. It was first published in 1879, for 400 customers.

980. Pioneers wishing to build in early Rochester could secure local bank mortgages. What rate of interest did they pay?

981. The Twenty-ounce variety of baking apple was first grown in this Monroe County village.

982. The Kodak bonus is based on a formula of an employee's wages earned over how many years?

983. As of 1982, which occupation had the most people licensed to practice in Monroe County: chiropractors, optometrists, architects, psychologists, or veterinarians?

984. Built in 1831 as the second hotel in Henrietta, it still stands today, now operating as this restaurant.

985. This stationery business opened its first store in the Powers Building, on the site where forefathers of the owners built Rochester's first home in 1812.

986. It's Rochester's fastest growing employer in 1984, with a CCS symbol on the Dow ticker.

987. In 1875, Wau Lee became the first Rochesterian from China. What business did he open?

988. This amusement park was set on a point, overlooking the bay to the west.

989. This was the first Rochester building to employ a passenger elevator.

990. In 1896, the editor of Rochester's Herald newspaper called it a "novelty work," and compared it to the Safe Liver Cure Pill fad. What product was he not impressed with?

991. Built in 1927, this structure would be torn down and replaced by Xerox Tower.

992. In 1810, which was the most valuable export from this region, at $2.50 a barrel: flour, pork, ashes, or whiskey?

993. United Auto Workers picketed two local car dealers in 1980. They went to court over this issue.

994. In the 1920's, John Priesecker sold this gourmet delicacy from a stand on Front Street. He trapped them in selected spots around the county.

995. Two gentlemen named Absalom Bishop and Thayer Codding got to the point in 1849 and invented the first one right here in Rochester. They promptly wrote about it.

996. When William Kimball made them at a site along the Genesee, they were sold under the names "Vanity Fairs" and "Sweet Caporals."

997. When 14 Rochester companies agreed to provide this for their workers in 1931, it was the first such organized effort in America.

998. It was originally known as the Pneumatic Signal Company.

999. In 1817, the Mansion House was built on Carroll Street as the first service establishment of its kind in the heart of the new settlement. What was it?

1000. Rochesterians make 3.5 million of these every day.

1001. The message "10-22-38, Astoria" was the first one in 1938.

1002. What Rochester dining establishment serves the "Garbage Plate Special," and what's on it?

1003. In 1982, Bausch & Lomb hoped to sell these to 5 million of the 35 million Americans who needed them.

1004. Rochester nurserymen Ellwanger and Barry filled one of the city's first major overseas export orders with a shipment of fruit trees in 1872. To what country?

1005. In 1833, Rochesterians in this line of work made one every four minutes. Today, high speed printers can knock out more than a thousand of these a minute!

BUSINESS & INDUSTRY

1006. Dentist Dr. J.B. Beers made history with the first use of this "precious" discovery in his Reynolds Arcade office in 1843.

1007. Tobin Packing made white hots packaged under what subsidiary label?

1008. In the late 70's, Eastman Kodak was taken to court in an anti-trust suit. Who was the plaintiff?

1009. What were the Knights of St. Crispin in the 1860's, one of the city's first and largest?

1010. 17,996 slabs of this were removed from Lincoln First Tower.

1011. It was once the Irondequoit Farmers' Grange building on Titus Avenue.

1012. In 1957 it produced 31 million gallons.

1013. In 1978, a business at 1455 University Avenue was closed, following an explosion. What was the business?

1014. Rochester's first railroad ran westward, linking Rochester with what city?

1015. What was the original name for the Xerox Corporation?

BUSINESS & INDUSTRY

1016. Rochester's Public Market is open for business two weekday mornings. Which two?

1017. What was George Eastman's profession before photography?

1018. Their motto was "Where Quality Predominates."

1019. Seth Green, one of America's first marine biologists, invented this device to enable him to examine his specimens in hand.

1020. Local nurserymen Ellwanger and Barry introduced 20th century America to this garden vegetable, known to botanists as "Raphanus sativus."

1021. The corn from Corn Hill was used to fatten animals for slaughter, producing two products that bore the Corn Hill brand name. What were they?

1022. The Rochester German Company, the city's largest in 1890, gave citizens a feeling of protection. What did they sell?

1023. From 1840 to 1850, it was one of the major industries in what would become Irondequoit, supplying raw materials for use in Rochester.

1024. Opened in 1975, the Park Ridge Hospital gets part of its name from its former location and name. What was it?

1025. What is Rochester's third largest employer?

BUSINESS & INDUSTRY

1026. Rochester was the smallest of 26 American cities selected to test market this home video game in 1982.

1027. In 1956, 8,222 Rochesterians decided to dabble in the stock market, buying what they all knew was a "sure thing." What did they buy?

1028. In 1977, what did Monroe County have more of, car dealerships or drug stores?

1029. This was the most important product made by wheat and rye farmers in the early pioneer days here, because it was easier to transport than grain.

1030. Bausch & Lomb began by making spectacles, but in 1875 they branched out by unveiling 5 brand new models of this product.

1031. By 1891, Stein Manufacturing of Rochester produced 75% of those used in America.

1032. Meyer Greentree and his wife opened the city's first mass production clothing shop. In 1842, 25 cents would buy a pair of these.

1033. Everyone associates Delco with parts for GM cars. Another Rochester firm plays a big part in the making of Rolls-Royces, Volvos, Fiats, and Renaults, to name a few. What's the company?

1034. During a lengthy lawsuit, Marketplace Mall developers threatened to build elsewhere. Where?

1035. The discriminating Rochesterian could choose to buy from one of three companies in 1886: Rochester Light, the Brush Company, or the Edison Company. What was the product?

1036. Eastman Kodak unveiled this photographic innovation in 1963.

1037. As early as 1900, it had earned the nickname "Sibs" among Rochesterians.

1038. Before its demolition, there were plans in 1959 to convert the huge New York Central station into this.

1039. In 1954, the city purchased space on 33 billboards along major suburban roads. What did the signs promote?

1040. In 1983, it boasted 800,000 members.

1041. Even with all his earnings, George Eastman bought stock in only one other company. In what local firm did he invest $50,000?

1042. It is far and away the most popular bottled wine sold in the greater Rochester area today.

1043. It's the name for Genesee beer's unknown ingredients.

1044. What were BU 8, CO 6, and FI 2?

1045. In 1954, the Hickok Company began production of this new safety device.

1046. Designed by a germ-conscious Rochester doctor, these were first used at Presbyterian Central Church services in 1894.

1047. The sealed can process was first used at the Cobb Preserving and Canning Company in Fairport. What was the first product to be canned?

1048. Early settlers in what is now Greece and Parma got quite a deal. Land was for sale at $2 an acre. How long did they have to make their first payment?

1049. It began as the Rochester Fruit and Vegetable Company in 1916.

1050. After all the records were destroyed in the blaze of 1904, 90% of Sibley's customers did this anyway.

1051. In 1880, two Rochesterians were employed as "pluggers." What was their job?

1052. George Selden designed his first automobile model in Rochester in 1906. What did it use for fuel?

1053. By the 1880's, this product grown and bottled around Irondequoit Bay was in great demand all along the East Coast for use as a medicine.

1054. Rochester area imbibers consume some 144 million each year.

1055. With 18 pumps, it's the largest in the county. In the 70's, what was it called?

1056. What were the Elmheart, Springwater, Edgewater, and Odenbach's?

1057. In 1923, George Eastman said, "Get the best men available. Never mind the cost." What professionals was he after?

1058. Founded in 1911 and sold in '79, it was one of the oldest of Rochester's "five-and-dimes."

1059. Amiel Mokhiber opened one of the city's first original fast food chains. What was the specialty called?

1060. Its forerunners were the Franklin Institute and the Athenaeum.

1061. His prison record notes a 3-year youthful offender sentence. Now his store earns $6 million a year selling records.

1062. In 1983, only one Rochester-based company paid its chief executive officer a salary of $1 million plus. Name the corporation and its millionaire.

1063. In 1914, this Kodak Park worker thought there was money to be made processing the film that George Eastman manufactured. Seventy years later, it's still a thriving business. What was his family name?

1064. What was the subject of the first book published by the Lawyers Co-op of Rochester in 1882?

1065. How much did Rochester, Fitzhugh, and Carroll pay for the 100 acres that is now downtown Rochester?

BUSINESS & INDUSTRY

1066. It's Rochester's only locally owned banking institution.

1067. In 1852, Rochesterian Jesse Hatch invented a machine that replaced this type of done-by-hand work, thus revolutionizing the shoe business.

1068. In 1908, Edward Halbeib began Northeast Coil Company by fooling around with electricity in the basement of his North Water Street home. By making such things as starting cranks and horns, he started the company, now known by another name.

1069. The first settlers in Genesee Country began receiving mail service by 1812. What did they pay for postage?

1070. No less than five of these establishments have burned in the town of Rush's history.

1071. For how long was radioactive steam released into the atmosphere at the Ginna plant in 1982?

1072. This shopping area in Pittsford still bears the name that was once given to the land that today is Pittsford and several surrounding towns.

1073. In the 70's, they had names such as "The Electric Walrus," "Mud Elephant," "Eastern Smoke," and "The Frog." What were they?

1074. Until 1921, large wagons lined Front Street selling a most precious commodity in the days before automobiles. The area was even named after this product.

1075. All safes made by Rochester's Sentry Company bear a unique construction feature. What is it?

BUSINESS & INDUSTRY

1076. Both Kodak and Xerox are ranked among the top 10 employers in New York State, New York City included. Where does each place within the 10?

1077. Because of the rapid expansion of business and industry there, a stretch of this road earned the nickname "The Miracle Mile" in the late 1950's.

1078. Vick Park A and B are named after a turn-of-the-century nurseryman, James Vick. What used to occupy space along those two streets?

1079. With strong connections to Eastman Kodak, it has been Rochester's largest law firm with origins dating back to 1875.

1080. It is the city's oldest surviving clothing manufacturer.

1081. What were Bausch and Lomb's first names?

1082. How many shoe stores are there in Marketplace Mall?

1083. A coat maker at Hickey-Freeman since age twenty, he would go on to be hailed as the most powerful labor leader in city history.

1084. This company began making fireworks in Ogden in 1930, and ended up making hand grenades for the war.

1085. It's claimed that these baby products were first developed in Rochester at the turn of the 20th century.

BUSINESS & INDUSTRY

1086. It was America's first indoor shopping mall.

1087. It's often referred to as "restaurant row."

1088. This fire in 1904 produced nearly $3 million in damage. What business was destroyed?

1089. The Sterling-Homex Corporation went out of business making these.

1090. 111,262 county residents do this every weekday.

1091. The village of East Rochester grew up around this industry.

1092. In 1950, it was the city's third largest employer.

1093. How much money, on the average, does an Eastview Mall merchant pay in yearly Monroe County taxes?

1094. $835,300 was stolen from a Doyle armored truck outside this factory in 1972.

1095. Still known for its biological specimens, this firm was known worldwide in the 1860's for its collection of meteorites.

1096. In 1932, many Rochesterians took to the street corners, selling these to try to survive.

1097. Whose motto was "Be big, be a builder"?

1098. What was the location of George Eastman's first factory?

1099. By 1890, half of the women in Rochester were enhancing themselves with these products.

1100. One out of every 7 working Rochesterians does this.

1101. Started in 1848, at a cost of $100,000, it served 80 people.

1102. In the 1820's, it was Rochester's second biggest industry, with 6 firms cranking them out at $800 to $1,200 apiece.

1103. Max Brickner was the first Jewish president in the history of this organization.

1104. Not usually associated with things nuclear, Eastman Kodak nevertheless developed a product in the 40's that prompted one military man to say, "It will give millions of people peace of mind." What was it?

1105. In 1919, men named "Potato Sacks," "Black Barry," and "Stack-em-up Joe" ran businesses in Rochester. What was their line of work?

BUSINESS & INDUSTRY

1106. How many exposures did the first Kodak film contain?

1107. In 1930 there were none. Today, the Rochester directory lists more than 100.

1108. It opened at the intersection of East Avenue and Elm in 1901. Its location was dubbed "Hoodoo Corner" because so many other businesses had failed so far away from the Four Corners. This one didn't. Name it.

1109. It's widely known that Stouffer Foods runs the Rochester Plaza Hotel, but who owns it?

1110. Current Science and Inventor, a national publication, called "inkless printing" one of the 10 major inventions of the year 1949. What was another name for this type of printing?

1111. In Rochester's first clothing factory, long before Muzak, Oren Sage kept his workers happy by doing this.

1112. In the 1850's, Ellwanger and Barry planted seeds from California, and within 15 years, 7 of these had grown to enormous size right here in Rochester.

1113. It was packaged and sold out of Rochester with the brand names "Pride of Dakota," "Granite," and "Corona." What?

1114. In 1867, laborers in this industry asked the county to abolish the practice of having inmates work on these products.

1115. In one day in 1982, 130 bottles of this were removed from Rochester store shelves in response to a nationwide panic.

1116. The Mill shopping mall took over a building once occupied by this department store.

1117. When Abelard Reynolds built the original Reynolds Arcade on Buffalo Street in 1828, the four-story structure with skylight was totally constructed without the use of this seemingly essential hardware. What?

1118. Before its tower was built downtown, where were Xerox offices located?

1119. The fire at the Eastman House was started by the spontaneous combustion of cellulose nitrate stock. What burned?

1120. The Institute of Optics, the only one of its kind in America, is located at what Rochester college?

1121. While the ones to the south now have the spotlight, the first upstate one was actually on the hillside overlooking Irondequoit Bay in 1830.

1122. Industrialist Howard Samuels built this company around a new technique for making vinyl plastics.

1123. In 1864, several Rochester stores were selling "false calves." What were they?

1124. The Wilmot family owns and operates three county shopping malls. Name them.

1125. In 1940, Schlegel brought one of its products to Strong Memorial Hospital, and a new era in energy conservation was under way. What was the product?

1126. After Wegmans dropped them, Loblaw's picked them up. But they still vanished from Rochester in June of 1973.

1127. What's the mailing address for the R.T. French Company?

1128. He invented the copying system that would ultimately lead to the Xerox Corporation.

1129. By 1957, there were 1.3 in every Rochester household.

1130. In 1893, it was the biggest department store between New York City and Chicago.

1131. What were Stein & Adler, Hayes & Brother, Greentree & Wile, and Rosenthal?

1132. During the war years, General Railway Signal produced some most essential war equipment. What?

1133. In pioneer days there was little machinery to be found in Rochester other than in the flour mills, yet some men were termed "mechanics." What do we call their trade today?

1134. Which was the last historic flour mill in operation in Rochester?

1135. The Rochester Button Company was the target of an unusual job action in 1937. What tactic did union employees use?

1136. What does CETA stand for?

1137. What happened to Fashion Park and Timely Clothes in 1970?

1138. They premiered on February 4, 1982, with a base price of $67.95.

1139. After making his product for Washington's Army, Abner Wakeles began this Rochester industry in 1812, opening a shop on Buffalo Street.

1140. As horses were used less and less in the city, downtown buildings used as stables were being replaced by these businesses in the 20's.

1141. During a dry spell in 1949, the city of Rochester purchased some of its water supply from this company which was pumping its own.

1142. Joseph Requa of Rochester invented "Requa's Battery" by joining 25 gun barrels together. Created at the end of the Civil War, this weapon has another name today.

1143. In the 1970's, it was a popular restaurant and night spot in the basement of the Xerox Auditorium.

1144. In 1950, realtor John Nothnagle unveiled a brand new home marketing technique. What was it?

1145. It's the oldest of Rochester's industrial giants.

1146. Enos Stone bought the first one from Nathaniel Rochester.

1147. From 1901 to 1905, two competitors came to downtown Rochester from Philadelphia and Syracuse to give Sibley's a run for its money. Name them.

1148. As of 1983, it was Rochester's largest with rooms for 900.

1149. How did George Eastman's company come by the name "Kodak"?

1150. The historic 140-year-old Corning House in Webster was torn down to make way for this.

1151. It's the biggest single reason that Italians and black men found it easier to get jobs in 1943.

1152. By 1908, the Chamber of Commerce had a new city slogan. "Rochester made," it said, meant this.

1153. He paid the bill for the University of Rochester's schools of music and medicine.

1154. Back in 1886, this corporation was the R.J. Strasenburgh Company, known as much for their chewing gum as for their chemicals. What is it today?

1155. It's Rochester's largest bank.

1156. Noted marine biologist Seth Green was also a Rochester businessman. In 1848, he opened up a shop on Front Street. What kind of store was it?

1157. In 1980, a national magazine sued Kodak for its failure to return 200 of the 2,000 slides it had processed for the publication. What was the subject of the slides?

1158. At last count, there were more than two dozen businesses offering this no longer unique way to say "I love you."

1159. Now city employees, these private businesses were first licensed by the city in 1838.

1160. It was Rochester's tallest building before Xerox Tower came on the scene.

1161. Today, this company sells a billion a year in 17 states, making it America's 8th largest.

1162. In 1815, the stagecoach provided "shuttle service" twice a week to this town, near what was becoming Rochester.

1163. What was the original name for Bausch & Lomb, Inc.?

1164. In 1979, it would have cost you $9 to sit in one for an hour.

1165. This chain was the first to open a suburban branch department store in a shopping plaza.

1166. in 1955, it was known as America's largest producer of hot dogs.

1167. What does RGRTA stand for?

1168. What color are National ambulances?

1169. The Chase-Pitkin stores used to go by a longer name. What was it?

1170. Dropping over $1 million into the local economy each year, this has local retailers calling it "Christmas in March."

1171. For more than a decade, this unlikely union represented employees at WOKR-TV.

1172. It's become a yearly tradition at the War Memorial, but Rochester's first one was held at the old Naval Armory in 1908, in the infancy of the industry.

1173. These two Irish and German immigrants started up the city's flowering nursery business.

1174. In the late 1960's, FIGHTON, a branch of the FIGHT organization, manufactured special parts for what local company?

1175. Who operates more ice cream stands in Rochester, locally owned Abbott's, or the Carvel national chain?

1176. A 1959 study found that this was more expensive in Rochester than in any other major city in the state.

1177. What was the first name of Sibley, the founder of the store?

1178. What's the official name for each of these Kodak products: instant film, x-ray film, its computer blood analyzer, and its video camera?

1179. Founded in 1884, it is one of Rochester's oldest banking institutions, distinguished by its time-temperature clocks.

1180. The current Pittsford home of Wolfe Publications is believed to have been the county's first, then known as "The Phoenix." The first what?

1181. As Rochester became a city, there were two abortive attempts to start this industry here, but no one could figure out how to import the raw materials quickly and cheaply. Name the industry.

1182. Kids play with them, smoking dads can't do without them, and Rochesterian J. Harry Stedman invented them.

1183. A Main Street clock marks the site of this. In its heydey one of the busiest in America, it still operates at that same site today.

1184. Casper Pfaudler, founder of the Pfaudler Corporation, had his humble beginning designing glass-lined holding tanks. What did those first tanks hold?

1185. Japanese imports and smaller models drove this local industry temporarily out of business in 1982.

BUSINESS & INDUSTRY

1186. Remnants of tropical storm Bret did $1 million worth of damage to this industry in 1981.

1187. Furniture maker Frank Ritter designed the first new model in 1887. He got no plaque, but neither did its users. What was it?

1188. A plaque dedicates the county's Hall of Justice to John Mastick who plied his trade in the upstate New York wilderness in 1770. A first in the area, what was his profession?

1189. Ebenezer "Indian" Allan built the first one in 1789.

1190. Which has more colleges within it, the U of R, or RIT?

1191. Begun along the Genesee in 1878, this company's first product was known as "Liebotschaner."

1192. From November of 1955 through January of 1956, Rochesterians went without their two daily newspapers. How come?

1193. Where did the name "Xerox" come from?

1194. By 1909, unions wanted stores to close by 6 p.m. They contended that owners wanted longer hours, not to attract more customers, but for what reason?

1195. In 1938, for the second time in its history, Rochester was seen as the new center of this industry. Lewis American Airways opened the plant on University Avenue. What was the product?

1196. In 1853, Rochester seamstresses formed Rochester's first clothing workers union. A walkout had produced a 25% daily wage increase. How much did that amount to?

1197. In 1916, you could buy one of these for your main dish at Callahan's Restaurant on North Water Street for 30 cents. And that included a potato!

1198. What symbol, atop a pedestal, marked the site of the Gerber Baby Food Company?

1199. What is the name for Eastman Kodak in France?

1200. In 1984, what does bus fare with a transfer cost a 14-year-old?

1201. The syrup comes from Atlanta, but it's mixed and bottled right here in Rochester.

1202. Driving along East Avenue into the city, one can see a lit sign looming above the center of the street in the distance. What does the 7-letter sign say?

1203. Before the arrival of Xerox, this was the biggest industry in the town of Webster.

1204. In 1901, Rochester brewery workers earned $13.25 a week. How much was that an hour?

1205. The official seal of Monroe County includes three symbols that represent key Rochester industries. Name the companies symbolized.

1206. The Hong Kong Restaurant now occupies a site formerly owned by two previous Alexander Street eating establishments. Name them.

1207. In 1899, a Rochester Jew and an Irish Catholic joined forces to revolutionize the men's clothing industry. What were their names?

1208. How did users of the first Kodak film go about getting their film processed?

1209. One Italian-American family is responsible for two of the city's commercially successful paisano favorites. Name the products.

1210. Perched atop Lawyers Co-op, Mercury may look like the FTD flower delivery man, but in ancient Greece, he was better known as the god Hermes. What was he the god of?

886. Self-service shopping
887. Xerox copier
888. Public transportation tokens
889. Eastman Kodak and Taylor Instrument
890. "A sangwich and a cupa coffee"
891. Pianos made at Aeolian in East Rochester
892. 111 East Avenue
893. 8% ($8,390)
894. 7 p.m.
895. Carlos Metidieri
896. Graham crackers
897. Greece Town Mall—85 (Midtown—84, Long Ridge—75)
898. Rochester's first suit
899. Fanny Farmer's
900. Uhuru
901. Ward's Natural Science
902. It bought the Rochester Transit Corporation.
903. The end of the Depression (9,000 new jobs under the NRA)
904. Brockport
905. Water!
906. Chamber of Commerce
907. Communications Workers of America (Rochester Telephone)
908. Owner Benjamin Forman
909. Potash; boiled down ashes from burned trees
910. $5.00
911. A piece of rubber; he found it in the street.
912. Instant mashed potatoes
913. Topper beer
914. The Casket
915. All made by Rochester's Pennwalt Pharmaceutical
916. George Eastman
917. The Sunday comics
918. Thirty
919. All are owned by Associated Dry Goods (ADG)
920. Smittey's Birdland
921. Curtice Brothers
922. 2 cents
923. Ragu spaghetti sauce
924. Farmers
925. Gannett and Sybron
926. Irondequoit melons
927. Politicians

BUSINESS & INDUSTRY ANSWERS

928. Hand-delivered mail
929. Beer
930. St. John Fisher
931. Northgate—1953
932. Bankers Trust
933. War bonds
934. City living
935. Cheesy Eddie's (cheese cakes)
936. French's mustard
937. Silk; silkworms populated mulberry trees.
938. Susan B. Anthony coins
939. Gambling parlors (casinos)
940. Dried apples
941. $2.00
942. Buttons
943. A 4-cylinder automobile
944. Amalgamated Clothing Workers Union
945. Sealing cans for canned goods
946. All of them
947. Brownie cameras, dubbed "Brownie's little baby" according to Kodak
948. Cherry House
949. Hookers and their "customers"
950. Jerseys made by Champion Products
951. Page Avjet
952. Rochester, Minnesota (smaller city, but has the Mayo Clinic)
953. Blown electrical fuse
954. Techniplex
955. Marshmallow
956. Apparatus Division
957. Wegmans Grocery Store
958. Stromberg owned the station, then WHAM-TV
959. Perinton
960. Chinese restaurants
961. The mail chute
962. Mail-order seed purchasing
963. The Spring House
964. Eastman Kodak
965. Greece (1,698—that's one in every 23 working people)
966. A city cab license plate
967. Hotels
968. The Hard-Working Dollar
969. Two-day weekend

970. McDonald's—21 (Burger King—20, Wendy's—11)
971. Plate glass windows
972. Schlegel Corp.
973. In-vitro fertilization
974. Milling flour
975. The Mill
976. Commercial airlines; it was the forerunner to American
977. "Backyard"
978. GM-Delco
979. Rochester telephone book
980. 7%; capital was not easy to obtain in a boom town.
981. Hilton
982. Five
983. Architects (140); psychologists (120); the rest all under 75
984. Cartwright Inn
985. Scrantom's
986. Computer Consoles
987. A laundry
988. Willow Point Park
989. Powers Building
990. The Kodak camera
991. Loew's Theater
992. Ashes
993. The dealers sold Toyotas; UAW wanted us to "Buy American."
994. Frogs' legs
995. The fountain pen
996. Cigarettes
997. Unemployment insurance
998. General Railway Signal
999. A tavern
1000. Phone calls
1001. Xerox copy
1002. Nick Tahou's; hots, beans, macaroni salad and home fries!
1003. Bi-focal contacts
1004. Japan, for Tokyo's Royal Gardens
1005. Gannett newspapers
1006. A gold tooth
1007. Arpeako
1008. Berkey Photo
1009. A labor union
1010. Carrera marble

BUSINESS & INDUSTRY ANSWERS

1011. House of Guitars
1012. Genesee Brewery
1013. An organized crime gambling parlor
1014. Batavia
1015. Haloid
1016. Tuesday and Thursday
1017. He was a bank clerk.
1018. Don & Bob's
1019. Fishing reel
1020. Radish
1021. Ham and bacon
1022. Insurance
1023. Logging
1024. Park Avenue Hospital
1025. The University of Rochester; approximately 7,000 employees
1026. Pac-Man
1027. Rochester Community Baseball stock
1028. Car dealerships, nearly 3:1!
1029. Whiskey
1030. Microscopes
1031. Caskets; it became National Casket Company the next year.
1032. Boys' pants
1033. Gleason Works
1034. Avon
1035. Electricity
1036. Instamatic cameras
1037. Sibley's
1038. A supermarket
1039. Shopping downtown
1040. Rochester Blue Cross
1041. Stromberg-Carlson
1042. Riunite Lambrusco, screwtop and all!
1043. The Genny-secret
1044. Old Rochester telephone exchanges (Butler, Congress and Fillmore)
1045. Seat belts
1046. Individual communion cups
1047. Corn
1048. Ten years
1049. Wegmans
1050. Paid their outstanding bills
1051. Manually connecting every city phone call; 3,000 a day!
1052. Kerosene
1053. Port wine

BUSINESS & INDUSTRY ANSWERS

1054. Cans or bottles of beer
1055. ElRancho Gaseteria
1056. All hotels on Ontario's shores
1057. Musicians (for the RPO)
1058. Neisner's
1059. The beef-amiel
1060. RIT
1061. Armand Schaubroeck
1062. Gannett; Allan Neuharth
1063. (Harry D.) Carhart
1064. Supreme Court cases
1065. $1,750.00 ($17.50 an acre)
1066. First National Bank of Rochester
1067. Stitching uppers to soles
1068. Delco
1069. 20 to 25 cents
1070. Hotels
1071. Two minutes
1072. Northfield (Commons)
1073. Boutiques
1074. Hay; Front Street Haymarket
1075. They're all the same height and width; only the depths change on different models.
1076. Kodak—4; Xerox—10
1077. Jefferson Road (between West and East Henrietta)
1078. Eight acres of tulips
1079. Nixon, Hargrave, Devans & Doyle
1080. Hickey-Freeman
1081. John Jacob and Henry
1082. 26
1083. Abe Chatman
1084. Antonelli Fireworks
1085. Baby shoes
1086. Midtown Plaza—1962
1087. Alexander Street
1088. Sibley, Lindsey & Curr
1089. Pre-fabricated homes
1090. Commute to work downtown
1091. Railroad car manufacturing
1092. Stromberg-Carlson
1093. None; the mall is in Victor, Ontario County.
1094. Kodak's Hawkeye plant
1095. Ward's Natural Science
1096. Apples
1097. WSAY radio
1098. State Street, now the site of Kodak offices

BUSINESS & INDUSTRY ANSWERS

1099. Cosmetics
1100. Works at Kodak
1101. Rochester Gas Light Company
1102. Shipbuilding
1103. Chamber of Commerce
1104. Radiation dose film badges
1105. Speakeasies
1106. 100
1107. Computer stores
1108. McCurdy's
1109. Alcoa Aluminum
1110. Xerography
1111. Reading them the newspaper
1112. Redwood trees (52 feet tall)
1113. Flour
1114. Shoes
1115. Extra-strength Tylenol capsules
1116. Edwards
1117. No nails; he used hickory pins.
1118. Midtown Tower—12th floor
1119. Old movie negatives
1120. University of Rochester
1121. Vineyard
1122. Kordite
1123. Stockings to cover up women's ankles
1124. Marketplace, Eastview and Greece Town malls
1125. Weatherstripping
1126. S & H Green Stamps
1127. One Mustard Street
1128. Chester Carlson
1129. Automobiles
1130. Sibley's
1131. Clothing manufacturers of 1850
1132. Explosive shells (bombs)
1133. Carpentry
1134. Daisy Flour Mill; now a restaurant
1135. A sit-down strike; it lasted more than a week.
1136. Comprehensive Employment Training Act
1137. Both went out of business
1138. Kodak's disc camera
1139. Shoes
1140. Gas stations
1141. Eastman Kodak
1142. Machine gun
1143. Shakespeare

1144. The Gallery of Homes; photos of homes for sale
1145. Bausch & Lomb—1853
1146. Lot—piece of land
1147. McCurdy's and Edwards
1148. Genesee Plaza Holiday Inn
1149. He invented it; he wanted a five letter word, beginning and ending with the letter "k".
1150. McDonald's restaurant
1151. World War II; they were moving into the city while other men were off to war.
1152. "Quality"
1153. George Eastman
1154. Pennwalt
1155. Lincoln First
1156. Fish market
1157. A Penthouse Pet of the Year nominee; Kodak said existing law prevented publication of "lewd" material.
1158. Balloon bouquets
1159. Garbage collectors
1160. Kodak Offices (Kodak Tower)
1161. Genesee Brewery
1162. Canandaigua
1163. Bausch & Lomb Optical Company
1164. A city taxi (that's going nowhere)
1165. McCurdy's (Northgate)
1166. Tobin Packing Company
1167. Rochester Genesee Regional Transit Authority
1168. Green
1169. Bilt-Rite Chase-Pitkin
1170. The Kodak bonus
1171. Teamsters
1172. The Auto Show
1173. Ellwanger and Barry
1174. Xerox
1175. Carvels—10 (Abbotts—7)
1176. Utilities (purchased from Rochester Gas & Electric)
1177. Rufus
1178. Kodamatic, X-omatic, Ektachem and Kodavision
1179. Columbia
1180. Tavern
1181. Cotton mills
1182. Fuzzy pipe cleaners

1183. Western-Union (in the Reynolds Arcade)
1184. Beer
1185. Aeolian Piano Works
1186. Xerox in Webster
1187. A dental chair
1188. Attorney
1189. Flour mill
1190. RIT—10 (U of R—8)
1191. Genesee Brewery
1192. A strike by pressmen
1193. Greek (xeros—"dry" and graphien "to write")
1194. So the owners could shop for themselves!
1195. The car; the 3-wheeled, 43-mpg Airmobile never made it. The owners went bust before mass production began.
1196. Twelve cents to 62 cents a day
1197. A steak
1198. A jar of baby food
1199. Kodak-Pathe
1200. 80¢—full fare
1201. Coca-Cola
1202. Sibley's
1203. Drying apples
1204. 25¢; they worked 53 hours a week!
1205. Kodak—a shutter; Bausch & Lomb—a lens; Gleason's—a gear.
1206. Montemarte and Yesterdays
1207. Hickey and Freeman
1208. They turned in the entire camera. When they got the prints back, the camera was also reloaded with new film. "You push the button, we do the rest," was more than a slogan!
1209. Bravo macaroni and Gioia spaghetti sauce
1210. The god of commerce (business and industry)

SPORTS

1211. In 1973, Gannett editor Desmond Stone called it "as unexceptional as a bingo gathering in a country church hall." What event was he describing?

1212. University of Rochester basketball posted a 24-45 record in its first 8 years of existence. It's an amazing accomplishment, considering what the team lacked. What were they sans?

1213. In both 1941 and '42, the *Times Union* sponsored a golf tournament. Each was won by a golf legend. Who were the winners?

1214. Royals coach Les Harrison outbid Cleveland and Youngstown for this man's services. The contract was for $5,000, but he would earn his lasting fame in Cleveland playing another sport. Name the player and the sport.

1215. A Jefferson High grad, he's the only Rochesterian to win a World Series game.

1216. In 1980, East and Penfield set a Section 5 record that still stands: least points in a basketball game. How many did they score combined?

1217. In 1925, the Rochester Centrals competed in the semi-pro American League. What was the sport?

1218. Only 12 NBA hoopsters have earned championship rings with more than one club. Arnie Risen of the Royals won his first in 1951. He earned his second in 1957. With what club?

1219. In 1967, Lancer Dennis Jones scored 2 goals in a game against Baltimore: a game the Lancers won 3-2. What's unique about his feat?

1220. Not known as a stellar first baseman, this ex-Wing would go on to major league fame as the successful manager who never signed more than one-year contracts. What's his name and nickname?

1221. This school's football team debuted with a 106-0 defeat to Cornell.

1222. Two former U.S. presidents have been inducted into the Oak Hill Country Club's "Hill of Fame." Name them.

1223. In '29, '30, and '31, the Red Wings won the pennant under the direction of this man, regarded by many of the old-timers as the Wings' greatest skipper.

1224. In 1913, a year before his National Open triumph, Walter Hagen was given a tryout by a professional team in another sport. He was finally told to practice hard and try again next year. What was the sport?

1225. Following his demotion from team captain, Red Armstrong was traded from the Amerks. To what team?

1226. It's the site of the Rochester Invitational LPGA Tournament.

1227. Silver Stadium and another league stadium were built using the same architectural model. In what city is the Rochester twin?

1228. Which two high schools play football annually for possession of the "Little Brown Jug"?

1229. On the first day that first baseman Harry O'Hagan became manager of the Rochester Broncos in 1902, he also recorded this historic first in Rochester baseball fielding history.

1230. In 1973, Rochesterians watched a semi-pro team that had changed its name from the Warriors to the Wolves just prior to the start of the season. What was the sport?

SPORTS

1231. He called the 1980 PGA at Oak Hill the biggest thrill of his career, despite his tenth-place finish.

1232. In 1971, former Public Safety Commissioner Harper Sibley, Jr. and furniture tycoon Harry Mangurian were both part owners of an NFL franchise. Which one?

1233. Rochester picked up two members of the Lake Placid miracle team in 1980. Name them.

1234. It began in Rochester in 1951, for young boys ages 9-13.

1235. How many 20-game winners have the Red Wings had since the 1941 season?

1236. It was first played on fields that would one day become Genesee Valley Park and home for the Freebooters team.

1237. It's now called the Caesar's Tahoe Professional Athlete of the Year Award. What was it formerly called when based in Rochester?

1238. It's the subject of much heated debate, but it's believed that Rochester ball player Richard Willis was the first to use this in a game, prompting some scientific study.

1239. This champion boxer and former onion farmer is perhaps best remembered for a fight he didn't win: a split decision loss to Sugar Ray Robinson.

1240. Royal guard Red Holzman is best remembered for his classic defensive battles against one of the NBA's all-time great playmakers. Name the opponent and his team.

SPORTS

1241. In 1971, the Lancers set a Guinness world record in just under 3 hours. What was the record?

1242. How long is the city's Lilac Festival footrace?

1243. The year he set a Wing record with 42 homers, he also set a record with 134 bases on balls. He's the all-time Wing home run king.

1244. In 1896, a new rage was the formation of sport clubs with names such as Anchor, Lake View, Newport, and Press Cycle. What was the activity?

1245. In 1911, this ethnic group organized a men's baseball team and called it the Hudson Stars.

1246. This company's products were advertised in the first modern Olympiad souvenir program in 1896.

1247. In the '58-'59 season, four Amerks were named to the first team league all-stars. Two would later return to coach the team. Name them.

1248. Where did Earl Weaver manage before he came to Rochester in 1966?

1249. They were WHEC's two sportcasters who worked during Rich Funke's absence in Florida.

1250. A proposed Rochester Flash match with the Springbok team in 1981 triggered a storm of controversy. What was the issue?

SPORTS

1251. When the International League first awarded the Governor's Cup, it was with the consent of the governors of three states with league teams. Name the states.

1252. Park Avenue's sudden curve along Vick Park and Oxford is directly attributable to this sport.

1253. At last count, there were 85 operating in the Monroe County area.

1254. During Luke Easter's Red Wing days, any Wing who homered received this as a prize.

1255. What was the name of the management company that ran the Rochester Lancers franchise?

1256. The Red Wings once had an Indian mascot. What was her name?

1257. What was Amerk Red Armstrong's first name?

1258. Where did Joe Crozier coach the season after he left Rochester in '68-'69 and what league was that?

1259. This superstar would play here with his national team in '73 to a half-filled stadium, only to return two years later with his American team, before the largest soccer crowd in Rochester history.

1260. She's the only woman to win the LPGA Tournament in Rochester under two different names.

1261. He earned MVP honors in '75 and '76 in Section 5 basketball, foreshadowing his future success just down the Thruway apiece.

1262. In 1855, some British immigrants formed the city's first teams and played matches in the public squares downtown. What was the sport?

1263. North Carolina State's David Thompson was the first to win College Basketball Player of the Year honors and this award in 1975.

1264. Rochester won the Calder Cup three out of four years from '65-'68. Who won it the other year?

1265. In 1867, it was said to be the city's favorite sport and its growing popularity could threaten baseball as the "national pastime."

1266. This team name was chosen from contest entries. The winner, 15-year-old Richard Paeth, received a $100 Victory Bond.

1267. Over its 80-plus years, the University of Rochester basketball team has posted more victories (76) against this intrastate rival than any other opponent in school history.

1268. Red Wing second baseman Dave Johnson would go on in the 70's to hit behind the two all-time home run hitting kings. Name them.

1269. During his off-seasons with the Royals, Bobby Davies took up this sport and became one of Rochester's finest at it.

1270. In 1911, Rochester hosted the first "owl tournament": the first time this sport was played in America under artificial lighting.

SPORTS

1271. Rochesterian Walter Hagen was the first professional golfer to ever reach this earnings milestone.

1272. In 1896, Rochester fielded a baseball team named after one of George Eastman's products. What was the team name?

1273. Rochester's Zeniths performed for five years in the CBA. How many times did they finish first in their division?

1274. Before coming to Rochester, Joe Altobelli played for Indianapolis against the Wings in the 1956 Junior World Series. He shared the outfield with a man who was just 5 years away from making history. Name him.

1275. In 1983, this Rochester product was used at 17 major league ball parks including Yankee, Riverfront, and Three Rivers Stadium. What was it?

1276. When he took the helm as Red Wings skipper, the press and fans knew him as "Bucky." Name him.

1277. In 1966, pro golfers Arnold Palmer, Bruce Devlin, Jack Nicklaus, and Doug Sanders staged an exhibition match at Oak Hill Country Club. Who won?

1278. This school's athletes got their nickname as a result of a student contest held when the collegiate sports program began in 1976.

1279. In May of 1981, the full attention of major league baseball and its fans turned toward Rochester. How come?

1280. Only 3 schools in Section 5 basketball history have captured titles in Class AAA, AA, and A. East and Madison did it. Who was the other one?

1281. Now coach of a Section 5 championship basketball team, he was the first member elected to the Rochester Track Club's Hall of Fame. Name him and his alma mater.

1282. Who played the most games in goal in Rochester American history?

1283. Holleder Stadium was once affiliated with what school?

1284. Musician Chuck Mangione grew up aspiring to be an athlete. Where did he have dreams of playing?

1285. This Rochester fighter recorded a knockout victory without ever throwing a punch. At the bell, his opponent charged across the ring, fell over the ropes and knocked himself out on a radio microphone!

1286. In 1978, women's tennis great Althea Gibson competed in Rochester. But the sport wasn't tennis. What was her game?

1287. "Daddy Wags" would later patrol the outfield in Candlestick Park, but in 1960 his home was Norton Street. Name this ex-Wing.

1288. The longest game ever played at Red Wing Stadium went 22 innings, with Rochester over Jersey City 3-2. It was an especially big game for Tom Poholsky. Why?

1289. Notre Dame placekicker Bob Thomas turned down a pro offer from the Los Angeles Rams and signed a contract with the now defunct World Football League, instead. What was the franchise?

1290. It debuted at the War Memorial in November of 1955, when Hans Schmidt met Verne Gagne, and 5,485 fans met "The Walking Iceberg," Yukon Eric Holmbach.

1291. In the waning days of the 1983-84 season, it was physically impossible for Amerk Mal Davis to set an AHL season scoring record. Why?

1292. She was the first to win the LPGA Golf Tournament in Rochester in 1977.

1293. Joe Altobelli managed the Red Wings for how many seasons?

1294. His poem "Riley On The Mound," the story of the pitcher who struck out Ernest Thayer's "Casey At The Bat," is now kept at the Baseball Hall of Fame in Cooperstown.

1295. This Rochester golf pro holds the course record on no fewer than six area courses, including Brook-Lea, Monroe, Happy Acres, and the Livingston Country Club in Geneseo.

1296. It was the War Memorial's opening event, lasting 79 days and including 6,000 local contestants.

1297. For the first time, in 1979, two schools from the same district were top seeds in Class AAA and AA of Section 5 basketball. What was the district?

1298. In the 1976 off-season, Buffalo Sabre Rick Dudley played for a Rochester professional team. What was the sport?

1299. Ed Fleming and Maurice Stokes of Rochester's Royals were two of the first in the NBA. First what?

1300. He's the only Red Wing skipper to run the club as both a Cardinal and Oriole farm team.

SPORTS

1301. In April of 1981, 5,600 fans were delirious at the War Memorial as this upstate favorite won the superwelterweight title over Rocky Moseley.

1302. Rochester Royals stars Bobby Wanzer and Bobby Davies hailed from the same alma mater. Name it.

1303. 50,000 pounds in one day in 1939 set a record as the largest undertaking of its kind in New York State history. 25 tons of what?

1304. In 1943, state labor inspectors found nearly one in 5 of these establishments violating child labor laws. What was the sport and the job?

1305. The original Americans uniform did not feature the current team logo. What dominated the front of the '56 Amerk jerseys?

1306. They were the first Rochester high school to win a Section 5 basketball tournament, back when only Class A teams competed in 1922.

1307. In 1961, John Powell led the Red Wings in battings, homers, and RBI's. The fans knew him by another name. What was it?

1308. What was (and is) the nickname for both the old Rochester Lancers and the new Rochester Flash cheerleaders?

1309. This 1971 University of Miami grad had a career decision to make: music teacher or pro golfer. This grad from Geneva chose golf. Name her.

1310. Viewers who played *Bowling For Dollars* at home had a nickname. What was it?

SPORTS

1311. Taking over at mid-season, he coached the Lancers to the NASL title in 1970.

1312. Doug Gibson is the only Rochester Amerk to do this twice, in '74 and '76. Do what?

1313. In the 30's, local yachters competed against the Yacht Club of Toronto annually for possession of a trophy much like the America's Cup. What was this one called?

1314. In Rochester, the teams are the Aardvarks and the Colonials. What's the sport?

1315. In 1941, the University of Rochester defeated Michigan State, Princeton, and Yale en route to an undefeated season. Name the sport.

1316. In 1916, Rochester pitcher Carmen Hill was the first to wear these on the mound.

1317. The only Amerk coach to be fired at the end of one season, he returned as coach by the first game of the next.

1318. From 1908 to 1928, when baseball was played on Bay Street, this slugger, known for his hitting prowess, was the only one able to homer over the right field scoreboard. Name him and his team.

1319. What do NFL players Bob Thomas and Eugene Goodlow have in common?

1320. It was first played in Rochester on Josiah Anstice's farm in 1893.

1321. This sport was banned in the City School District for thirty years (1909-1939).

1322. This Rochester Royal was an NBA champ as a player, and later as a coach and general manager. Name this three-time champ and the other club where he earned rings #s 2 and 3.

1323. Who were the Russers, the Oxfords, and the Dutchtown Vays?

1324. In 1945, the Rochester Royals paid $40,000 for this.

1325. From 1923-51, he compiled a 866-115 lifetime record, tossing 61 no-hitters and guiding his team to the world championship twice. Who was he?

1326. This 1973 Amerk enforcer was once suspended after he continued to punch a Nova Scotia Voyageur who was already unconscious on the ice.

1327. In 1900, Rochesterians turned out in droves for three annual parades. Decoration Day and Labor Day prompted two of them. The third was tied to a sporting event. Name it.

1328. Coach Red Blaik created quite a stir when he converted star end Don Holleder from end to quarterback of this college football team in 1955.

1329. Manager of the Wings in 1943, what was "Pepper" Martin's real first name?

1330. In 1897, Rochester police stormed the diamond with Kid Gannon on the mound. They arrested and booked "The Kid" and six of his Rochester teammates. What was the charge?

1331. Before signing a pro contract, Cardinal Mooney and St. Bonaventure star Glenn Hagan contemplated a show biz career with this team.

1332. During the 1973 season, Gordon Turner set U of R scoring records for most points in a game and most points scored in a season. What was the sport?

1333. In 1858, teams known as The Live Oaks, and the University Club battled teams from Brooklyn and Buffalo. What was the sport?

1334. In 1961, Trent Jackson tied a world high school record, running the 100-yard dash in 9.4 for Franklin High. The mark had previously been held by this great Olympic sprinter.

1335. Amerk goalie Bobby Perreault is remembered for a nervous habit he'd display on the ice during a game, for good luck. What did he often do?

1336. In 1964, Rochesterians Mike Austin, Doris Fuchs, and Trent Jackson all found themselves in Tokyo. What were they doing there?

1337. In his entire career, golfer Terry Diehl was able to capture only one PGA Championship, that coming in his rookie year, 1974. What was the city of that event?

1338. When Walter Hagen won the U.S. Open in Chicago in 1914, he was employed by the Oak Hill Country Club. What was his job?

1339. In the stretch of '66-'68, Rochester had three Rookies of the Year in the International League: a first baseman and two outfielders. Name them.

1340. From 1900 to 1908, they were known as the Broncos and then as the Beau Brummells.

SPORTS

1341. This football play made its first appearance locally in 1906.

1342. The Rochester Royals basketball franchise moved to what city in 1957?

1343. Through the 1950's, Rochester amateurs boxed in "mission bouts." They were affiliated with what local high school?

1344. How long had the American Hockey League been in existence before Rochester joined in the '56-'57 season?

1345. East High star 6'11" Walt Dukes went on to set basketball scoring records at Seton Hall. But in 1951, he flunked his army induction physical. Why?

1346. In 1971, Joe Altobelli's Red Wings won the Junior World Series. What team did they beat out?

1347. How many stars are there on the Rochester Amerks insignia?

1348. The current site of Strong Memorial Hospital on Crittenden Boulevard was once the site of a sports stadium. What was the sport staged there?

1349. In 1972, he was the highest paid Rochester Lancer, earning $7,000 for the season.

1350. In 1898, for the second time, the Rochester ball club finished out its season in a Canadian city. Which one?

SPORTS

1351. *Golf Digest* magazine rated this local course in the top 30 greatest in America.

1352. This all-time favorite Red Wing hit 66 career home runs. He died years later, a bystander in a Cleveland bank shootout.

1353. This East Rochester legend won the 1950 United States Amateur Championship in Minneapolis. Name him and his sport.

1354. The Rochester Zeniths played in what basketball league?

1355. Bobby Ketchum was the first to crack the roster of the Rochester Lancers soccer team. First what?

1356. Usually associated with another sport, this Rochester businessman was instrumental in committing Toronto as the Amerks' parent club in exchange for eventual home ownership.

1357. The St. Louis Cardinals threatened to pull its franchise out of Rochester and move it closer to its Midwest home. What was the city being considered?

1358. It was the Wings' worst opening day defeat: a 23-1 loss to the Tidewater Tides in 1982. Who was the starting Wing pitcher tagged for 6 runs in less than two innings?

1359. It was first introduced in the city at the YMCA gym at the turn of the century. Name the sport.

1360. In 1983, for the first time, a Section 5 Class AAA team, Webster Thomas, set a season and tournament record. What was it?

SPORTS

1361. In 1865, Rochester fielded two teams for this sport: the Atlantics, for those east of the Genesee, and the Pacifics, for those west of it.

1362. When the Amerks won the AHL playoffs in 1983, hundreds of fans toasted the event by getting a drink from "Frank." Who or what was "Frank"?

1363. In 1971, the International League All-stars played their exhibition game in Rochester. Who was the opponent?

1364. Steve Demeter played third base for the Wings from '64-'68, but had some great years against the Wings before and after. Name the teams.

1365. This genial golfer was a real gallery pleaser when he won the U.S. Open at Oak Hill in '68.

1366. Which Rochester sports team was named after team names at the University of Windsor, the alma mater of one of the owners?

1367. Hailing from Dutchtown, Bill Klem made his mark in national sports as "The Great Arbiter," with his boast, "I never missed one in my life." What was his profession?

1368. Rochester's Billy Knipper headed west to the brickyards for the first five years of its existence, but never won this event.

1369. It's Monroe County's largest bowling alley with 80 lanes.

1370. In 1921, Rochester Tribe player Maurice Archdeacon set a world record sprinting a distance in 13.8 seconds. Where did "Archie" run?

1371. Community Baseball purchased the Red Wing franchise from St. Louis in 1956. What was the price?

1372. This high-scoring superstar was just 18 in his first season with the Lancers, and couldn't always keep the shirt on his back.

1373. Hard to believe today, but in 1921, '22, and '23, the Red Wings finished second to this International League team.

1374. This college's nickname comes from wildlife native to its first Rochester campus.

1375. Rochesterians who won the local Soap Box Derby advanced to national competition in Ohio. What was the city?

1376. In 1948, Rochesterian Ross Virgo was selected to the United States Olympic team for the London games. What was his event?

1377. In 1980, County Manager Lucien Morin said in proposing the purchase of this, "At $1,000 an acre, that's a steal!"

1378. A War Memorial favorite, this Rochester Royal won NBA Rookie of the Year honors in 1955-'56.

1379. The name came from the notion that kids played hookey and sneaked a peek at the game through the outfield fence. Rochester's was one of the first in the minor leagues.

1380. This professional team made its local debut with a win over the Sheboygan Redskins. Name the sport.

1381. They were commanders of troops supplied by natives for the Roman army. They're also the names for athletes at this college.

1382. The Rochester Amerks spend nearly $40,000 a year for this.

1383. Gymnast Doris Fuchs appeared in three consecutive Olympic contests from '56-'64. Name the cities.

1384. On July 26, 1960, Red Wing Frank Verdi was struck by a bullet while coaching. Where was the game being played?

1385. Driving and Crittenden parks were just two horse racing tracks that operated within the city of Rochester. Prevailing laws, however, made one aspect of the outdoor entertainment illegal. What was a no-no?

1386. Many hearty turn-of-the-century Rochesterians took part in "century marathon runs." How long were these endurance races?

1387. Over the years, the Amerks have had five NHL parent clubs. Name them.

1388. From the 20's to the 40's, Rochester women formed a team called the Filarets, generally acknowledged as the best in the upstate area. What was the sport?

1389. Leo Lyons once coached a Rochester semi-pro football team that played in a league that would one day evolve into the NFL. Name that Rochester entry.

1390. He's the all-time Amerk penalty king, leading his nearest competitor by 375 minutes!

1391. This American League umpire has also earned a living as a professional wrestler.

1392. Who were Poholsky, Jablonski, and Rupulski?

1393. He preceded Earl Weaver as Red Wing skipper from '63-'65.

1394. Hockey made a short-lived appearance in Rochester in the 1920's. A makeshift rink was set up. At what existing sports facility were games played?

1395. This golfing doctor won the U.S. Open at Oak Hill in 1956.

1396. From 1910-20, a great football rivalry sprang up because of the interurban railroad that linked Rochester with Geneva. What two schools squared off?

1397. In the '79-'80 season, Joe Crozier returned to coach against the Amerks in the AHL. What was his team, and would it or the Amerks end up with a better season record?

1398. In 1899, Rochester's first public golf course was laid out in South Park (soon to be Genesee Valley). Duffers had a most unusual hazard when playing: groups of animals moving across the fairways. What kind?

1399. It was August, 1977, and 20,000-plus packed Holleder Stadium to see the Lancers play soccer. It was one of the largest crowds in Rochester sports history. Who was the opponent and who won?

1400. He's the all-time Red Wing leader in games played, but does not hold a single game or season hitting record.

1401. He was the only Rochesterian ever to be named to an all-American football team. This wide receiver did it in 1954.

1402. Rochester Hustler first baseman Wally Pipp went on to play for the New York Yankees. Before a Yankee game in 1929, he asked to be benched for a headache. Who replaced him?

1403. Now a major league manager, this Wing outfielder hit .333 in '54 to lead the league in batting and the team in homers and RBI's.

1404. At an Olympic trial in Los Angeles, Trenton Jackson finally went head-to-head with the man billed as "the world's fastest human," former Dallas Cowboy Bob Hayes. Who won in 1964?

1405. In the 40's and 50's, Rochesterians were treated to weekly fight cards held at this fraternal organization's hall.

1406. He was the first person ever elected to the National Softball Hall of Fame.

1407. As a Red Wing, this major league manager won the International League batting crown in 1960, but never would play a game in the major leagues.

1408. This Livonia resident moved to Rochester and promptly became so good at his sport that he was barred from competition in the city at the tender age of 18. Name him and what he played.

1409. The '63 Wings were overloaded with first basemen: veterans Luke Easter and Steve Bilko, and a "younger" player who was shifted to the outfield to begin his last 3 years as a player. Who was he?

1410. Famed women's golfer Babe Didrikson once played the Oak Hill course, but her first Rochester appearance involved a different sport altogether. What was the sport?

SPORTS

1411. This golf legend still holds the Oak Hill course record with an 8-under-par 64.

1412. True or False? The Rochester Americans got the nickname "Amerks" because fans were cheering for star player Stan Smyrke.

1413. Walter Hagen won $300 for this in 1914.

1414. His fame would come on the gridiron as one of pro football's throwingest quarterbacks. But in 1938, he was snaring groundballs as a shortstop at Red Wing Stadium.

1415. When Nancy Lopez arrived to compete in the 1978 LPGA, she was gunning for a women's pro record for consecutive tournament victories. When she won the tournament, it was how many in a row?

1416. In 1980, this 15-year-old was voted Sportswoman of the Year by the Rochester Press Radio Club while still a student at The Harley School.

1417. How did the Rochester Zeniths get their name?

1418. This Rochester goalkeeper plugged chewing tobacco and posed for *Playgirl*.

1419. With all Rochester caught up in the patent medicine craze, one entrepreneur named a sports team the "Hop Bitters" in 1890, as a promotional tool for his product. What was the sport?

1420. In the '78-'79 season, the Amerks played "Traktor," the Russian team. There was only one incident. This Amerk jumped off the bench onto the ice and decked a Russian with one punch.

1421. Who holds the Rochester and International League record for runs batted in?

1422. They have won more Section 5 basketball titles than any other school.

1423. Sure-handed guard Bob Davies invented this basketball maneuver in the 1940's while still at Seton Hall.

1424. Where did Silver Stadium get its name?

1425. What did Amerks Stan Smyrke, Dick Gamble, and Murray Kuntz all have in common?

1426. The Royals' NBA championship season interrupted a string of 5 out of 6 crowns for this team still in the NBA, but now in a different city. Name the team.

1427. The Rochester Express played what professional sport?

1428. In what town is the Happy Acres Golf Course?

1429. In the '82-'83 Calder Cup season, this song became the Amerks' theme, played every time they skated onto the ice between periods.

1430. Known for his belly-first slides, this outfielder who'd later manage the Wings was the first to wallop a home run over the center field fence at the Norton Street park.

SPORTS

1431. When this 5'4" Binghamton third baseman played at Rochester's Culver Field at the turn of the century, he hit them where Rochester players weren't positioned. Who was he?

1432. When the Milwaukee Brewers play the Baltimore Orioles in 1984, the two managers, Joe Altobelli and Rene Lachemann, share something in common. What?

1433. The 1978 Rochester Red Wings were managed by two former major league superstars in the same season. Name them.

1434. Known for his homers that were able to clear tall fences with a single jerk, this Red Wing nicknamed himself "Superjew."

1435. When Rochesterian Bob Thomas kicks his 542nd point, he'll set a Chicago Bears team scoring record. He'll surpass what star of NFL and AFL fame?

1436. Rochester's Italian community wanted to present Red Wing slugger George Puccinelli with a brand new car. But he wouldn't accept the one they were giving him. Why not?

1437. He's a six-time world champion and the only man over fifty to win a world championship.

1438. Dick Sierens has been on the field at Silver Stadium longer than any player or manager. What's been his "position" since 1940?

1439. At the turn of the century in Rochester, red flower pots were used for these.

1440. In December of 1979, a team of RIT students and faculty set a world record. Doing what?

1441. In their first year at the Norton Street stadium in 1929, what place did the Red Wings finish in?

1442. In 1973, the Amerks were tagged with this nickname for their rough play under coach Don Cherry.

1443. He came to the Amerks a free agent purchased for $1,500 by the Maple Leafs. By the time he was through, he would end up #3 in all-time goals, #2 in points, and #1 in assists.

1444. The 1954 Rochester Red Wings needed to travel through U.S. Customs to play four of their league opponents. Who were they?

1445. Before Mike Neer took over as U of R basketball coach, this man held the position for 19 years.

1446. The Sheehy brothers, Tom and Mike, have each generated their fair share of high school and college headlines. In all, they've attended 5 schools from 9th grade on. Name them.

1447. Coming back from a near crippling farm accident, he's the only Red Wing to toss two 9-inning no-hitters.

1448. Although he went on to star as an offensive lineman with the Giants, Mooney and Notre Dame grad Jeff Weston was originally cut in August of '79 as a defensive tackle by the team that drafted him. Name the team.

1449. This former Aquinas High swimmer and Bishop Kearney Spanish teacher set a world record for the indoor mile in 1978.

1450. What was the name of Rochester's last semi-pro football team?

SPORTS

1451. When Amerk Mal Davis set a goal-scoring season record, he eclipsed a mark that had stood for 10 seasons. Who had held it?

1452. They still have the winningest percentage of any professional sports team in Rochester history.

1453. Which Rochester sports arena has the largest seating capacity?

1454. After a big league career in Cleveland and 3 years in Buffalo, Luke Easter came to play in Rochester. In '63, team management tried to get the ageless one to reveal that fact with a $10 enticement for each year of his age. How much did they pay?

1455. Everyone knows that Morrie Silver was the first president of Community Baseball. But who succeeded him while still a local politician?

1456. When Millie Martorella gained fame as a pro bowler, it was with her maiden name. What was it?

1457. Why is the lakeshore along RG&E's Russell Station a favorite spot for fish and fisherman?

1458. Rochester has more of these per capita than anywhere else in America.

1459. Fire destroyed the Rochester Jingoes' ball park in 1897. In what Canadian city did the team finish its season?

1460. He won 374 games in the National League, but after retirement he worked for a time as a bartender at the Home Plate, a sports bar on South Avenue.

1461. When the Lancers play the Indians in high school sport, the game is in what town?

1462. It's 26 miles 385 yards long, beginning and ending near the downtown YMCA.

1463. The Royals won a 7-game NBA championship in the '50-'51 season. Who was the opposition?

1464. Among starters, he set an all-time Red Wing season record with a 2.18 earned run average in 1980. Two other Orioles are ranked #s 2 and 3. Name all three.

1465. Hi-pockets Kelley still holds the Rochester hitting record for a game, banging in 9 RBI's for the Rochester Tribe in 1919. How many of his hits were home runs?

1466. The Red Wings' first "community-owned" manager, this jack-of-all-trades pitched, hit, and caught, as well as managed for the team in 1957.

1467. Sent as a sore-armed pitcher, he played only half a season for Rochester in the summer of '41. Still, this outfielder hit .326 during his stay. The rest is history.

1468. By today's standards, the pitching staffs of Rochester and most ball clubs at the turn of the century were unusual. How many pitchers did Rochester's club have, and why?

1469. In 1968, she set a world record for a league bowling average with a 219 at North Park Lanes.

1470. Before their current locations along the outfield foul lines, the Red Wing and visitor's bull pens were located where?

1471. How many times did Rochester win the CBA title?

1472. The Red Wings set a baseball record for the longest played game: 33 innings. Who was their opponent and who won the game?

1473. This flamboyant character has the Amerk record for most penalty minutes by a goalie. He did it in '76-'77.

1474. Before the 1972 season, with no NHL parent club, Coach Don Cherry put together a club by studying rosters with this newspaper sportswriter.

1475. In the 1980's, basketball games between these two high schools sold out the War Memorial three times.

1476. Rochester's ball club captured the Eastern League pennant at the Bay Street park for 3 years straight beginning in 1906. What was the team name?

1477. Two of the most daring outdoor activities every young child learns, these were both introduced as formal sports in Rochester in 1879.

1478. New York Islander coach Al Arbour played what position as a Rochester Amerk?

1479. This NBA team is the grandchild of the Rochester Royals.

1480. Although the lake had been there for ages, Rochesterians didn't begin this until 1850.

1481. In 1943, he was the reddest of Wings with a .337 average and MVP honors as the team's shortstop.

1482. Local sportswriters were instructed to hence use the word "discs" in their articles after a typographical error gave new meaning to those "flying" around the War Memorial. What were the discs?

1483. For more than a decade his name has meant football and baseball at Cardinal Mooney.

1484. This turn-of-the-century heavyweight actually staged an exhibition bout, then donned a uniform and played first base for Rochester.

1485. This common sports marketing practice may well have begun here when these were admitted free in 1885.

1486. Who replaced Harry "The Hat" Walker as Red Wing manager when he was called to manage the Cards in '55?

1487. It began in 1961 in Rochester, with 4 teams and 140 boys turning out in the fall.

1488. He played five years with the Amerks, from '76-'80, scoring 166 points. Now he coaches the Junior Amerks.

1489. On Thanksgiving Day 1950, a record crowd of 23,609 saw this high school battle St. Benedict's Prep to a 7-7 tie.

1490. Voted to the all-time Red Wing team, this infielder of the 20's and 30's earned his name from the glasses he sported.

1491. It's the sport of the Rochester Wheels team.

1492. One of the most popular Lancers, he named his son after Dragan Popovic, even though the coach and he were always feuding. Who was he?

1493. He's the Amerks' all-time iron man with a record not soon likely to be broken: 571 games played.

1494. If you're sitting in Section 15 of the War Memorial for a game, you're closest to which street exit?

1495. In 1966, this Red Wing known for his home runs blasted one out in the final game of the season vs. Syracuse to give the Wings a pennant.

1496. After his stellar play in 1978, he would come back to coach the Amerks for one game—a loss. Name him.

1497. In the early sixties, an object with a hole in it was placed above the Red Wing Stadium right field fence. Red Wings hitting a home run into the hole would win a cash prize. No one ever did. What was the object?

1498. This Rochesterian won 4 consecutive British Opens and 75 titles in all.

1499. This Amerk scored 41 goals on his way to Rookie of the Year honors in the '58-'59 season.

1500. There are two Rochesterians enshrined in the Basketball Hall of Fame in Springfield, Mass. Name them.

1501. When the Orioles won the '83 World Series, Joe Altobelli became the second Red Wing manager to win both the Junior and World Series. Who was the first?

1502. Which Amerk coach, Joe Crozier or Don Cherry, has won more Calder Cups?

1503. The Red Wings Class AA farm team is now Charlotte. But it used to be somewhere else. Where?

1504. It still stands as a Red Wing attendance record: an opening day crowd of 19,006 fans. They had come to see Southworth's Wings begin the drive for a fourth pennant. The year was?

1505. Rochester ball player Fred Lewis hit .412 in 1887, but no one today counts that as a team hitting record. He had help. How?

1506. In 1965, three of the biggest names in golf staged a head-to-head match at Oak Hill Country Club in an exhibition. Name them and who finished last.

1507. Mike Nykoluk and Earl Balfour scored the first two in the War Memorial.

1508. She rolled the first perfect game in Women's Pro Bowling Association history in 1967.

1509. Showing devotion above and beyond the call, this Amerk found his future wife behind a concession counter at the War Memorial.

1510. What did Red Wings Enos Cabell, Steve Demeter, and Pete Ward all have in common?

1511. Rip Collins and Specs Toporcer were part of a 1929 Red Wings infield that set an all-time world record with 225 double plays in a season. What were Rip's and Specs' real first names?

1512. There are 30 in the Monroe County area.

1513. In 1977, Franz Beckenbauer of the Cosmos called it "a nice place to grow potatoes."

1514. What's the longest Amerk win-streak? They've done it twice: in '65 and again in '73-'74.

1515. The 1940 Rochester Red Wings won the league pennant with 4 of them during the whole season.

1516. Which city park has the most tennis courts?

1517. In their inaugural year, it took the Rochester Amerks seven games before they had accomplished this.

1518. On the team insignia, the red wings on the baseball are on which side?

1519. Originally, Ray Hickok first awarded his belt in 1949 as a trophy for the winner of a particular sporting event, not for sportman of the year. What was the sport?

1520. 1966 was the first time that Rochester Community Baseball had ever been able to achieve this.

1521. How did the name "Red Wings" come about?

1522. Pitcher Johnny Antonelli was drafted in 1948 by the Boston Braves out of what Rochester high school?

1523. True or false? George Eastman liked to watch pro hockey.

1524. High school athletic teams in Monroe County compete in what New York State sports division?

1525. This Amerk coach known for his aggressive style saw it reflected in his pet dog, a pit bull terrier named "Blue."

SPORTS ANSWERS

1211. An Amerks' hockey game
1212. A coach
1213. Ben Hogan and Sam Snead
1214. Otto Graham—football
1215. Johnny Antonelli
1216. 8
1217. Basketball
1218. Boston Celtics
1219. He scored both goals FOR Baltimore.
1220. Walter "Smokey" Alston
1221. University of Rochester—1889
1222. Dwight Eisenhower and Richard Nixon
1223. Billy Southworth
1224. Baseball. He tried out as a Phillies' pitcher.
1225. Springfield
1226. Locust Hill Country Club
1227. Columbus, Ohio
1228. East Rochester and Fairport
1229. Unassisted triple play
1230. Football
1231. Terry Diehl
1232. Miami Dolphins
1233. John Harrington and Eric Strobel
1234. Little League baseball
1235. None
1236. Polo
1237. Hickok Belt
1238. A curve ball
1239. Carmen Basilio
1240. Bob Cousy—Boston Celtics
1241. Longest played soccer game—176 minutes
1242. 10 kilometers
1243. Russ Derry
1244. Bicycling
1245. The Poles
1246. Eastman Kodak
1247. Steve Kraftcheck and Rudy Migay
1248. Elmira
1249. Bob Hillman and Scott Murray
1250. Apartheid; Springbok was a South African team.
1251. New York, New Jersey and Maryland
1252. Harness racing; the road ran along a curve in the old Union track.
1253. Bowling alleys
1254. "Luke Easter Sausage"
1255. Blue & Gold
1256. Princess Red Wing
1257. Norman

SPORTS ANSWERS

1258. Vancouver—Western Hockey League
1259. Pele; Team Brazil and the Cosmos
1260. Nancy Lopez, Nancy Lopez—Melton
1261. Roosevelt Bouie (Kendall HS, Syracuse U.)
1262. Cricket
1263. The Eastman Award
1264. Pittsburgh
1265. Croquet
1266. Rochester Royals
1267. Hobart
1268. Hank Aaron (Atlanta) and Sadaharu Oh (Yomuiri)
1269. Golf
1270. Tennis
1271. $1,000,000.00
1272. Brownies
1273. 4
1274. Roger Maris
1275. French's mustard
1276. Earl Weaver
1277. Palmer; two-under-par 70
1278. Nazareth Golden Flyers
1279. A federal court case to avert a strike was heard here.
1280. Fairport
1281. Trenton Jackson—Franklin High
1282. Bobby "The Cat" Perreault
1283. Aquinas Institute
1284. Baseball in Yankee Stadium
1285. Ossie Sussman
1286. Golf; she dropped out after two rounds of the LPGA.
1287. Leon Wagner
1288. He pitched all 22 innings and won!
1289. Jacksonville Sharks
1290. Pro wrestling
1291. He was called up to Buffalo.
1292. Pat Bradley
1293. Six—1971-1976
1294. Foster Brooks
1295. John Calabria
1296. National Bowling Congress
1297. Rush-Henrietta (Sperry and Roth)
1298. Indoor box lacrosse
1299. Black pro basketball players
1300. Clyde King; 1959-62
1301. Rocky Fratto
1302. Seton Hall
1303. Carp, caught in one net out of Irondequoit Bay
1304. Bowling; pinsetters

SPORTS ANSWERS

1305. A large letter "R"
1306. East High
1307. Boog
1308. Dancers
1309. Mary Dwyer
1310. Pin Pals
1311. Sal DeRosa
1312. Win the AHL MVP award
1313. The Canada Cup
1314. Rugby
1315. Basketball
1316. Glasses
1317. Don Cherry (1971-72, '72-'73)
1318. Babe Ruth; *Baltimore*
1319. Both are McQuaid grads.
1320. Golf
1321. Football
1322. Red Holzman; New York Knicks
1323. All Rochester pro or semi-pro football teams
1324. Payroll, for the entire team!
1325. Harold "Shifty" Gears
1326. John Wensink
1327. Opening day of baseball season
1328. Army
1329. John
1330. Playing baseball on Sunday
1331. Harlem Globetrotters
1332. Basketball
1333. Baseball
1334. Jesse Owens
1335. He kissed his ring.
1336. All were part of the U.S. Olympic team.
1337. San Antonio, Texas
1338. Caddy
1339. Mike Epstein, Curt Motton and Merv Rettenmund
1340. Rochester's baseball team
1341. The forward pass
1342. Cincinnati
1343. Aquinas Institute
1344. Twenty years
1345. He was too tall!
1346. Denver
1347. Three
1348. Horse racing; Crittenden Park was a half-mile track.
1349. Carlos Metidieri
1350. Ottawa
1351. Oak Hill

SPORTS ANSWERS

1352. Luke Easter
1353. Sam Urzetta—golf
1354. Continental Basketball Association
1355. American player
1356. Morrie Silver
1357. Omaha, Nebraska
1358. Mike Boddicker
1359. Basketball
1360. They were undefeated.
1361. Baseball
1362. The (Frank) Calder Cup
1363. New York Yankees
1364. Toronto and Syracuse
1365. Lee Trevino
1366. Rochester Lancers (owner Charlie Schiano)
1367. Baseball umpire
1368. Indianapolis 500
1369. Olympic Bowl
1370. Around the bases
1371. Half a million dollars
1372. Branko Segota
1373. Baltimore
1374. U of R Yellowjackets; plentiful in the dandelion fields of the Prince Street campus
1375. Dayton
1376. Boxing
1377. Craig Hill Country Club; the county didn't buy it.
1378. Maurice Stokes
1379. Knot Hole Gang
1380. Basketball. The Royals won 108-75.
1381. Monroe Community College Tribunes
1382. Hockey sticks! (The same as the Royals' 1945 team payroll!)
1383. Melbourne, Rome and Tokyo
1384. Havana; the last American baseball game to be played in Cuba
1385. Pari-mutuel betting was illegal.
1386. 100 miles
1387. Toronto, Montreal, Vancouver, Boston and Buffalo
1388. Basketball
1389. The Jeffersons (or Jeffs)
1390. Red Armstrong
1391. Ken Kaiser
1392. All ex-Red Wings (Tom, Ray and Eldon)
1393. Darrell Johnson
1394. Red Wing Stadium
1395. Cary Middlecoff
1396. University of Rochester and Hobart
1397. New Brunswick; they did—first place; Amerks finished fourth.

SPORTS ANSWERS

1398. Sheep grazing on the grass
1399. New York Cosmos; they did, 2-1.
1400. Estel Crabtree (934 games)
1401. Don Holleder
1402. Lou Gehrig, who proceeded to play a record-setting 2,130 games
1403. Bill Virdon
1404. Hayes (10.1), Jackson (10.2) in the 100 meter
1405. The Elks Club
1406. Shifty Gears
1407. Jim Frey
1408. Irving Crane—billiards
1409. Joe Altobelli
1410. Basketball
1411. Ben Hogan
1412. False; more likely, Amerks is to Americans what Canucks is to Canadians.
1413. PGA Open Championship check
1414. Sammy Baugh of the Washington Redskins
1415. Five
1416. Golfer Jamie DeWeese
1417. They were owned by TV retailer Dick Hill, who sold Zeniths!
1418. Shep Messing (Rochester Lancer)
1419. Baseball
1420. Ron Garwasiuk
1421. Rip Collins (180 in 1930)
1422. East High
1423. Behind-the-back dribble
1424. From Community Baseball's first president, Morrie Silver
1425. All left wingers
1426. Los Angeles (then, Minneapolis) Lakers
1427. Softball
1428. Webster
1429. *Freeze Frame* by the J. Geils Band
1430. Pepper Martin
1431. Wee Willie "hit 'em where they ain't" Keeler
1432. Both are ex-Red Wings.
1433. Ken Boyer and Frank Robinson
1434. Mike Epstein
1435. George Blanda
1436. He wanted a more expensive model!
1437. Irving Crane
1438. Groundskeeper
1439. Golf cups (holes)
1440. Fastest time running across America
1441. First, their 2nd straight pennant
1442. Broad Street Bullies
1443. Bronco Horvath

SPORTS ANSWERS

1444. Toronto, Ottawa, Montreal and Havana
1445. Lyell Brown
1446. Tom (McQuaid HS and U. of Virginia), Mike (East High, Syracuse U. and St. Bonaventure)
1447. Dave Vineyard (1966-67)
1448. Miami Dolphins
1449. Dick Buerkle
1450. Mustangs
1451. Murray Kunz; 51 goals
1452. Rochester Zeniths
1453. Holleder Stadium
1454. $520.00
1455. Congressman Frank Horton
1456. Ignizio
1457. Warm water released lures fish closer to shore.
1458. Bowlers
1459. Montreal
1460. Grover Cleveland Alexander
1461. Irondequoit
1462. Rochester Marathon
1463. New York Knicks
1464. Mike Boddicker, Mike Flanagan and Dennis Martinez
1465. Four in a row
1466. Cot Deal
1467. Stan Musial
1468. Four, all were starters—there were no relief pitchers!
1469. Millie Ignizio
1470. Behind the left-center field fence
1471. Twice; '78-'79 and '80-'81
1472. Pawtucket Red Sox; they did.
1473. Jim Pettie
1474. Hans Tanner
1475. East and McQuaid
1476. Hustlers
1477. Bicycling and roller skating
1478. Defenseman
1479. Kansas City Kings (formerly the Cincinnati Royals); they changed the team name to prevent a conflict with the baseball club.
1480. Swimming in it
1481. Red Schoendienst
1482. Pucks
1483. Ed Nietopski
1484. Gentleman Jim Corbett
1485. "Ladies Day"; all "except those in carriages" were admitted free.
1486. His brother, Fred "Dixie" Walker
1487. Pop Warner football
1488. Barry Smith

SPORTS ANSWERS

1489. Aquinas Institute
1490. "Specs" Toporcer
1491. Wheelchair basketball
1492. Mike Stojanovic
1493. Dick Gamble
1494. Broad Street
1495. Mike Epstein
1496. Ron Garwasiuk
1497. A billboard replica of a mitt
1498. Walter Hagen
1499. Billy Hicke
1500. Bobby Wanzer—player; Les Harrison—contributor
1501. Billy Southworth—St. Louis Cardinals
1502. Crozier 3—0
1503. Elmira
1504. 1931
1505. Walks counted as hits, and batters were allowed four strikes!
1506. Palmer, Player and Nicklaus; Nicklaus was high man; Palmer and Player tied to win.
1507. Rochester American goals; 1956
1508. Millie Ignizio
1509. Red Armstrong
1510. Third base
1511. James and George
1512. Golf courses
1513. The Lancers' field at Holleder Stadium
1514. Nine games
1515. Managers (Southworth, St. Clair, Crabtree and Kaufman)
1516. Genesee Valley—8
1517. Won a game; they began 0-5-2.
1518. Originally right, but now left.
1519. Boxing; it went to the winner of a middleweight championship fight.
1520. A profit at year's end ($161,000)
1521. They became the 1928 farm team for the St. Louis Cardinals (or Redbirds)—hence Red Wings.
1522. Jefferson
1523. False. He liked to hunt big game for his sports amusement.
1524. Section 5
1525. Don Cherry

1526. She once said, "Any advertising is good. Get praise if possible, blame if you must, but never stop being talked about."

1527. According to city laws, how many dogs are you allowed to own and keep at your home in a residential area?

1528. How long does it take for the Changing Scene restaurant to make one complete revolution atop the First Federal Plaza Building?

1529. In 1940, this Rochester businessman sought the Republican nomination for U.S. president, receiving 33 convention votes on the first ballot, but eventually losing out to Wendell Wilkie.

1530. Rochesterian Georgette Protheroe authored *Georgette's Journal of Natural Living*. Where does this home nutritionist get the majority of the foods she advocates eating?

1531. How old was George Eastman when he stopped going to school?

1532. In the 1970's these were the most popular boy's and girl's names in Rochester; they still are.

1533. How many Thruway exits are there in Monroe County?

1534. Although he's gained his fame and infamy in politics, he's also an accomplished free-lance writer with works published in *Family Weekly*, *Catholic Boy*, and *Playboy*.

1535. For Rochester's first settlers the recipe was simple: boil three barrels of tree sap into one and add some yeast. What had been created?

1536. What do Rudyard Kipling, Winston Churchill's mother, and Susan B. Anthony all have in common?

1537. In the 1984 Rochester phone book, are there any people with the last name "Kodak," the name Eastman invented?

1538. The statue of Mercury is poised holding a bag in one hand alongside him. What does the bag contain?

1539. Rochesterian Adolph Stuber invented the Colorama: an 18-by-60 foot transparency that can vividly display a Kodak color photograph to thousands of people each day. Where is Colorama located?

1540. Born in 1930, he's earned a Guinness world record while spending most of his life behind bars.

1541. Completed in 1969, this urban renewal housing complex began as a call for action from Rochester's newest civil rights organization.

1542. Rochester's Jewish community opened it in 1949, serving 100 children.

1543. In the 1900's, some Rochester ministers refused to record the dates of marriages. Why?

1544. What do you do at Maple and Glide?

1545. There are four in Monroe County, the largest and oldest in Mendon with 400 quite permanent residents.

PEOPLE & PLACES

1546. Dr. Edward Mott Moore is often referred to as the "father of Rochester's parks." Where is his monument located?

1547. His turn-of-the-century curio shop on Mill Street featured Custer's last battle flag, two-headed calves, New York's first electric chair, and jars and jars of snakes.

1548. Which of these buildings are registered as county landmarks: Xerox Tower, Midtown Plaza, the Gannett Building, and Lincoln First Tower?

1549. How long is the term for a New York State Supreme Court justice?

1550. What religion did Susan B. Anthony believe in?

1551. Up to the 1930's, this building housed Rochester's post office, draft board, the Prohibition control office, and the F.B.I. What does it house today?

1552. He went to the University of Georgia on an athletic scholarship and hoped to become a doctor while competing as a pro athlete. His second career appears to be broadcasting instead.

1553. He arrived in Mendon in 1829 with the first of his 27 wives.

1554. After 57 years, Aquinas High School received a new addition in the fall of 1982. What was added?

1555. In the 1890's, a staple of the downtown "noisescape" was the blast of the fog horn at the Kimball Tobacco plant. It went off precisely on the hour at the start and end of the work day. What times did it blow?

1556. It was a state law at the turn of the century. Whenever a rider on a horse raised his hand, the operator of an automobile had to do this.

1557. While the first settlers who came to the Genesee valley abided by 10 of these, the Seneca Indians who had lived there were said to have had 157. What?

1558. At the turn of the century, most of the land north of Ridge Road was still swampy. Many people were stricken with what they termed "Genesee fever." Today, we'd call it this.

1559. This silent film star, now living in Rochester, was featured in a 1965 *Playboy* article entitled, "The History of Sex in the Cinema."

1560. This former Xerox board chairman would later negotiate the unpopular return of the canal to Panama.

1561. Rochester Gary Beikirch received a Congressional Medal of Honor for his acts of valor in which war?

1562. With street names like Glasgow, Edinburgh, and Grieg, it's easy to see that the first settlers of Corn Hill were predominantly of this descent.

1563. In 1925, the Sea Breeze Natatorium was a favorite recreation spot. The 300-by-125-foot swimming pool used Lake Ontario water heated to 75 degrees. What was then added to the water?

1564. This club was started in 1900 with 20 members, long before there were even good roads in Rochester.

1565. In what theater would you find a quarter-of-a-million-dollar Zeiss projector?

1566. There were an average of 27 a day on county roads in 1982.

1567. It was a coffee house and counseling center. From 1975-84, it sponsored Ground Hog weekends, and its Welcome Summer Arts Festival grew into what now is the Park Avenue Festival. What was it called?

1568. She once dubbed a portion of her vast collection "Rochester's Tiniest Suburb."

1569. He was the largest vote-getter among presidential candidates in Monroe County history, pulling more than 205,000 votes.

1570. He once said, "All I had in mind was to make enough money so that my mother would never have to work again."

1571. This outlaw of the 1980's earned his nickname from the chain stores he held up.

1572. The eagle statue overlooking the Genesee behind the War Memorial bears tribute to Rochesterians who fought in what war?

1573. These four words are written on the wall near the judge's bench in every courtroom in the Hall of Justice.

1574. In 1900, they were the second largest nationality in the city of Rochester.

1575. In 1921, Rochester's War Chest became the Community Chest, and later adopted this current name.

1576. Known as "The Jersey Leaper," he traveled with a trained bear on a chain and a pet fox on a rope.

1577. Of these, a federal official in 1980 said, "I don't see much question that eventually it will win public acceptance."

1578. This downtown seat of knowledge was once known as the Duffy-Powers Dry Goods Store.

1579. The Federal Building is named in honor of this United States Senator.

1580. It's the official perfume of the Lilac Festival. What's it called?

1581. What is the official name of the 50-foot-tall structure that towers above Manhattan Square Park?

1582. What do the names of Cardinal Mooney, Bishop Kearney, and McQuaid Catholic high schools have in common?

1583. What was the first auto speed limit in Rochester, set by state law?

1584. This county building complex began as a sanitarium in 1910. It was named from the Indian word meaning "never discouraged."

1585. What are the colors of the Monroe County flag?

PEOPLE & PLACES

1586. It happened between 5:29 a.m. and 5:33 a.m., more than one a minute, on March 17, 1981.

1587. He was the first president of what would eventually become RIT.

1588. As the two-party system sprang up, Rochester's German and Irish immigrants tended to enroll as Democrats. Why?

1589. In 1968, Laplois Ashford was the first black to win a citywide election. To what position was he elected?

1590. Although Barber Conable's congressional district included much of greater Rochester, it also included this town in Genesee County: his hometown.

1591. What color is the single light that shines in the Kodak office tower?

1592. For $2,000, he purchased 1,143 feet of Durand-Eastman beach, accidentally sold by the city. He wanted to open a "Hawaiian paradise," complete with boardwalk and admission fee. Who was he?

1593. Overlooking the Genesee, it's the oldest Victorian style one in America.

1594. Until Rochesterians were able to make their own, Irondequoit Bay was a major source of this household product, chopped and "harvested" by the wagonload. What was it?

1595. This religion was founded by the followers of the Fox sisters and their "rappings."

PEOPLE & PLACES

1596. This nationally known inventor was among the first to buy one of George Eastman's film cameras.

1597. Seven of Rochester's first 20 mayors all came from this profession.

1598. They first appeared outside downtown stores in the Christmas season of 1902.

1599. Originally known as "York," this Canadian city was "born" fifty-three days before Rochester, on March 6, 1834.

1600. A former Rochesterian was one of the 52 Americans held hostage in Iran in 1980. What was his name?

1601. Rochester had a thriving flying club in 1893. What did its members own?

1602. In 1983, who made more money: the district attorney or a county court judge?

1603. This Rochester bank was the first to receive official designation as a Rochester landmark.

1604. Spinster Florence Dailey may be the most infamous Kodak stockholder of all time. No one knew of her holdings until after she died, alone, in 1966. How much was her Kodak stock worth?

1605. Mahin Sadrai promised she would leave the country as soon as her semester at RIT ended in 1980. Why did she have to leave?

1606. What does the "A.M.E." stand for in Corn Hill's AME Zion Church?

1607. These traffic signs made their debut at downtown intersections in the mid-1950's.

1608. This health organization can be found on Christmas Seal Drive.

1609. Name the 3 public high schools in the Greece school district.

1610. Why did Frederick Douglass first call his newspaper "The North Star"?

1611. Traveling by train to Washington in 1860, he stopped in Rochester for a moment to greet 15,000 admirers at the station. The Rochester *Union and Advertiser* wrote that he was "... more agreeable than his pictures ... led us to believe."

1612. There were supposed to be two things happening continuously at the Liberty Pole, but they never quite worked properly. What's not going on?

1613. "One with God is a majority," is inscribed on the base of his statue near Highland Bowl.

1614. Eighty years before "I'd rather be in Rochester," the Chamber of Commerce had another slogan to encourage the workers at the city's emerging industries. What was it?

1615. If the people in Webster are "Websterites," and those in Brighton, "Brightonians," what do you call the people from Gates?

1616. In 1906, the city of Rochester was plagued by several episodes attributed to the "Black Hand." What's it known as today?

1617. William George Burrill became bishop of Rochester's Episcopal Diocese at this church in 1984.

1618. Open enrollment in 1963 began this controversial education practice in Rochester.

1619. Centuries before Women's Liberation, it was the custom of these Genesee valley people to give the children the mother's, not the father's, family name.

1620. Who owns and operates a vehicle with the New York State license plate M-1?

1621. It was the familiar name for the Lake Ontario Shore Railroad line constructed in 1876.

1622. A star local athlete, he was killed in action evacuating the sick and wounded from a battle site in Vietnam in 1967.

1623. As George Eastman is to Kodak, Louis A. Wehle is to what Rochester company?

1624. This Wild West showman has three of his sons buried in Mt. Hope Cemetery.

1625. Under the city's alternate street parking plan, what hour do cars switch sides of the street?

1626. While serving time for extortion, he signed a prison protest letter objecting to Christmas furloughs for Watergate figures H.R. Haldeman and John Erlichman.

1627. Pioneers Nathaniel Rochester, Edwin Scrantom, and Levi Sibley all shared a common hobby that found them joining the same group. What was the hobby?

1628. Whose likeness stands atop the monument in Washington Square Park downtown?

1629. What number bus route runs from Charlotte to Park Avenue?

1630. Why is the pedestrian bridge over the Genesee River downtown shaped like the letter "Y"?

1631. This stretch of land then owned by the city, now the county, was originally called Britton Field in 1921. What is it now?

1632. George Eastman was immortalized by the federal government on the face of a United States postage stamp. What was the stamp's value?

1633. Which came first in Rochester: East or West High School?

1634. What is Midge Costanza's real first name?

1635. Taking in the entire county population of 1983, how many people in ten have at least 4 years of college education?

1636. Named after the editor of a temperance newspaper in Seneca Falls, these were first worn locally by Susan B. Anthony.

1637. This Rochester chapter held its first meeting in March 1981. Thirty people attended, opening the meeting with no less than three verses of "My Country 'Tis of Thee."

1638. For 18 years in the early 1900's, George McLaughlin ruled this empire from a second floor office at Main and St. Paul in the heart of downtown. What was his business?

1639. Born in a log house in Monroe County in 1825, Antoinette Brown Blackwell was the first woman parishioner in America to become one.

1640. In honor of its humble origins in a farm field on the outskirts of Rochester, the University of Rochester named this as its official school flower.

1641. Before he made aviation history in Keuka of the Southern Tier, he worked in Rochester as a bicycling Western-Union delivery boy.

1642. Because of its use of wrought iron beams from France and brick for its construction, the Powers Building of 1865 was the first west of the Hudson to be able to claim this.

1643. Of Rochester he wrote: "I know of no place in the Union where I could have located at the time with less resistance or received a larger measure of sympathy and cooperation." Who was the author?

1644. With an all-steel frame, the Granite Building was Rochester's first.

1645. Was Judy Weis a pro bowler, a congresswoman, or Miss New York State, 1953?

1646. In a New York State report, this was once referred to as the "way station to Attica."

1647. What was the nickname for Vincent Massaro?

1648. He came to the city as a fresh-air kid from Bedford-Stuyvesant and ended up president of FIGHT in 1979.

1649. She came to Rochester in 1899 with hatchet in hand to promote the cause of temperance.

1650. On the first Tuesday of each November, the County Board of Elections spends $105.75, all in nickels and dimes! Why?

1651. Where is the "Poet's Walk"?

1652. It was used on West Avenue for the first time in 1886, and the locals dubbed it "dude pavement."

1653. This term applied to a growth rate of 23 per 1,000 in Rochester of the late 1940's.

1654. It's believed LaFayette, Aaron Burr, and the king of France all tipped at least one at this Rochester tavern, now an East Avenue landmark.

1655. "That I can do and I will," were his last words on November 13, 1829.

1656. In 1905, any arrested Rochesterian who did not speak or understand English was officially listed by police as being of this ethnic group.

1657. Rochester is one of only ten cities in the entire nation to have earned this designation from the National Municipal League.

1658. It boasts Rochester's largest Orthodox Jewish congregation.

1659. In 1981-82, this school district paid the most, $3,368 per student, for its students' educations.

1660. Some Rochesterians of the 1860's were particularly bothered by an unwelcomed visitor known as "the midge." What was the midge?

1661. Rochester's Corinthian Hall was the site of the National Dress Reform Association's meeting in 1863. Five-hundred women attended. What was the topic up for discussion?

1662. What does NTID stand for?

1663. After one term, Ken Keating lost his Senate seat to this man in 1964.

1664. In 1889, the city provided a shelter for unwed mothers. What was it called?

1665. How many Amtrak trains pass through Rochester daily?

1666. In 1972, Rochester was second only to St. Petersburg, Florida, with the nation's highest percentage of this age group.

1667. How did George Eastman sign his first name?

1668. Long before Mr. T., Rochester had its own "A Team," and "B Team" for that matter. Who were they?

1669. What were the first names of Swedish-born Stromberg & Carlson?

1670. Joseph Smith came to Rochester to get his book published. It was published in Palmyra instead. What was the title?

1671. Was Jose Iturbi a Lancer midfielder, a Philharmonic conductor, or founder of the Ibero-American League?

1672. What does the acronym "BOCES" stand for?

1673. Rattlesnake Pete was a saloon keeper, but also a supplier for some geniuses of modern medicine and science. This giant of French medicine turned to Pete for snake venom to perform his experiments.

1674. What was Mayor Tom Ryan's occupation before he entered politics?

1675. The urn bearing the ashes of George Eastman is set in a pink marble monument. Where is it located?

1676. In 1981, he was Rochester's largest landowner, with downtown properties worth $4 million and 3,500 apartment units across the county.

1677. Above its doors is the inscription: "Erected MDCCCCXXII for the enrichment of community life."

1678. How tall is the dome at the Strasenburgh Planetarium?

1679. How many countries are represented on Midtown's Clock of Nations?

1680. Susan B. Anthony and Frederick Douglass once tangled in an argument over the right to vote. What was the issue in their disagreement?

1681. He's served as the city's Episcopal bishop for 14 years ('70-'84).

1682. What do DeLeon McEwen, Raymond Scott, and Bernard Gifford have in common?

1683. When it debuted on downtown streets in 1913, this traffic regulation got bad reviews.

1684. On his way to work from East Avenue to State Street, George Eastman set his watch every morning by the clock in this downtown belltower. It still stands today as part of a park.

1685. In 1931, one in 4 Rochesterians did this at age 16.

1686. The current Liberty Pole is not Rochester's first. One was built, 101 feet tall, at the Main and Franklin site in 1859. It lasted until 1889. What happened?

1687. It has the largest collection of Iroquois artifacts in the world.

1688. At the turn of the century, how were city streets plowed and cleaned?

1689. What do "Fantasy Swings," "Elliot's Nest," "The Fun House," and "Westminster Park Inn" all have in common?

1690. Rochester's fifth mayor, Elisha Johnson, donated a piece of his land for the site of a new city hall. It was never built on the site, but the land remains as this park in the heart of downtown.

1691. It's supposed to be done once every ninety years in Rochester, but current budget projections say it can't happen in each case for another 683 years.

1692. It began in 1869 as the Free Methodist Chili Seminary and was later renamed after its founder.

1693. The Pope-Hartford, Pope-Toledo, and the Searchmount were some of the first of these to appear on the streets of downtown in 1898.

1694. In the 1880's, the neighborhood along North Clinton, Avenue D, and St. Paul was known as "The Butter Hole." Why?

1695. For decades, Rochesterians tracked the lifespan of James Hard, the oldest living survivor of the Union Army of the Civil War. He finally died in 1953. How old was he?

1696. This Main Street building housed the city's first post office and skylit shopping area. The name of it still applies, though now to a reconstruction.

1697. He once wrote in a national magazine, "It's more fun to give money than to will it."

1698. The sculpture that stands alongside the Eastman Theatre ramp garage at Main and Scio was said to resemble a sense of movement related to dance. So U of R sculptor Archie Miller named the work after a famous dance team. What's it called?

1699. From 1871-1915, Rabbi Max Landsberg spearheaded this movement throughout the world.

1700. Frederick Douglass lived to see the University of Rochester unveil a bust of his likeness to be kept on permanent display. What was unusual about it?

1701. Charles Dickens, Tom Thumb, and Daniel Webster all held sway at one time or another on the stage of this theater, named for its architectural design.

1702. Returning from a "family" meeting in 1957, this Rochester produce wholesaler told the press: "I don't know anything about what the papers say about gangsters there. I didn't see any." Who was he?

1703. Based on the 1980 census, which has a larger population: the city of Rochester or Mt. Hope Cemetery?

1704. From 1913—1963, Rochester's original zoo was located where?

1705. Until his death, Nathaniel Rochester served as a supervisor for what county town?

1706. In 1920, it was hailed as the city's "greatest piece of public health work." Dr. George Goler examined 7,369 children over 3 months. What was he checking?

1707. This example of Art Deco bears more than a passing resemblance to Manhattan's Chrysler Building.

1708. Because of their marches and street singing, this group was at first thought to be satirizing organized religion. They were arrested twice in 1884, and disbanded, only to return later as a Rochester institution.

1709. Is Rochester's Los Flamboyanes a Spanish-American dance troupe, a high-rise apartment complex, or a Puerto Rican restaurant?

1710. He was elected to the Senate the same year Rocky took over in Albany.

1711. What did the Rundel Fund help construct?

1712. Who were Kenneth Bianchi and Angelo Buono?

1713. In a 1974 *Upstate* article, this organized crime figure was listed as one of Rochester's ten most powerful people, taking his place alongside bankers, politicians, and executives.

1714. In 1936, he was on trial for murdering a 14-year-old boy. The sentence: confinement to his house for the rest of his life. But he broke out of his Brockport home and died running into a car. Who or what was he?

1715. In 1973, this was proposed as a means of traveling from Rochester to Toronto in one-and-a-half hours.

1716. These women were given the right to vote in the Genesee valley nearly 300 years before Susan B. Anthony came along.

1717. How long would Mayor Tom Ryan have to serve in office to be the Rochester record holder for longest term . . . until what year?

1718. By 1911, it was Rochester's most popular full name, with 53 listings of it in the directory.

1719. This "Washington replica" was the original home of the city's Visitors' and Convention Center.

1720. Name the Rotary Camp in Penfield along Irondequoit Creek.

1721. Famed architect Claude Bragdon designed Rochester's Chamber of Commerce Building and the train station, but it's believed he also designed 50 of these in the city.

1722. What was unusual about the Rochester subway line as it began in Brighton?

1723. The names Rush Rhees and George Whipple were, and still are, synonymous with this Rochester institution whose buildings still bear their names.

1724. Before the Civil War, one of its major routes went up what is now West Henrietta Road to Mt. Hope, and ultimately to a dock on the Genesee River.

1725. A post in the center of the pedestrian bridge over the Genesee notes distances "M*A*S*H-style" to several cities. What do the cities have in common?

1726. Myer Greentree was the city's first. A tailor by trade, he's now viewed as the father of Rochester's community of this religious persuasion.

1727. He was the Indian chief that finally deeded over the infamous hundred-acre tract to Oliver Phelps. An upstate community still bears his name.

1728. Who was Frederick Augustus Washington Bailey?

1729. Its average daily population in 1983 was 394. That's 120 over what it was designed to house.

1730. This school began in 1876, when Rochesterian Gilman Perkins sought a teacher for his daughter and found that 60 other local children needed the same special kind of instruction.

1731. Rochesterian George Selden filed a patent for his invention in 1879, only to lose a lawsuit that would change the course of history for America and a Midwest city. What was his invention?

1732. Rochesterians used to hang colored pieces of cloth from their front doors as a signal to neighbors. What was the message?

1733. William "Billy" Carter was the first "resident" of this planned community along the Genesee that overlooked downtown Rochester of 1838.

1734. In the 1970's, a story circulated through Rochester of a lady in grey who stood near Holy Sepulchre Cemetery on Lake Avenue hitchhiking, only to disappear into thin air. Where, according to the myth, did she want to go?

1735. Rochester's early settlers got along without one article of apparel now considered essential. These would only be worn in the winter.

1736. From the time he came to the city, he lived on Alexander Street, Hamilton Street, and South Avenue where he ran a "station" near Highland Park for the underground.

1737. Jerre Mangione wrote this account of his growing up in Rochester's Italian neighborhoods.

1738. Long before Wild Bill Hagey, this rather elderly Rochesterian would roam the stands at Norton Street, leading cheers by calling out players' names.

1739. Born in 1898, she's known as the "Mayor of Strathallan Park." A night spot high above that street is named in her honor. Who is she?

1740. According to a 1980 study, this percentage of Rochester's Jewish community is affiliated with no synagogue at all.

1741. He donated $2.5 million to MIT, under the name of "Mr. Smith." It was eight years before they found out who Mr. Smith really was. Who was it?

1742. In 1981, 4 in every hundred high school students in the county were doing this.

1743. It's the familiar name for the county's animal shelter.

1744. What are the "painted ladies"?

1745. In 1970, planners saw it as a downtown shopping area of small shops lining a cobblestone road along the Genesee.

1746. How many commercial runways are there at the county airport?

1747. Elected by the largest plurality in county history, this man was drummed out of office by the same voters in his re-election bid.

1748. In 1980, much attention was paid to U of R exchange student Deng Zhifang. Why?

1749. The City of Rochester once operated a "pest house." What was its use?

1750. Kodak workers first received this in the spring of 1911.

1751. Sarah R.D. Dolly, MD was the first in the city in 1880.

1752. In the 1880's Rochester had a downtown fountain that featured a statue of a man holding out a glass filled with the pure fountain water. A dentist had come up with the idea as a psychological ploy. What was the idea?

1753. Rochester's Jaycees were twice expelled from their national organization in 8 years. Why?

1754. For nine years Albion's Charles Howard was a mainstay annually in city department stores. He even opened a college in 1938 and taught James Cagney and Edward G. Robinson his craft. What was he?

1755. In 1940, this was the city's official flower, not the lilac.

1756. Whose epitaph reads: "If you seek his monument, look about you. *Si monumentum requiris, circumspice*"?

1757. This revolutionary was born in Russia but spent most of her life in Rochester. She was one of the featured characters in Warren Beatty's *Reds.*

1758. Though others were credited later on, Jacob Myers invented one that was used on a trial basis in Rochester in 1896. We've used them at least once a year, every year since.

1759. This term for politically-motivated public works projects is said to have originated in Rochester.

1760. New York State Democrats picked this future U.S. president to be their governor at Rochester's Convention Hall.

1761. Cornelius Vroman is a legend in Clarkson for doing something continuously for five years, beginning at age 17, and living to tell about it. What did he do?

1762. Who or what was a "Manitou"?

1763. In 1978, gadabout Walter Carnahan offered a $100 prize to the RIT student who could come up with the best design for this mode of transportation.

1764. For years, he enjoyed weekly luncheons with four women known as the "Lobster Quartet," and even subscribed to *Vogue* so as to be able to converse more with them about the latest in women's fashions. Who was he?

1765. These three buildings comprise the Civic Center Plaza.

PEOPLE & PLACES

1766. Rochester's first settler, Ebenezer Allan, practiced a rather unconventional belief. What was it?

1767. In the 1890's, the owners of the Wilder and Powers buildings locked in heated competition. What was at stake?

1768. This world-famous newspaper publishing tycoon operated the *Journal* in Rochester in the 1920's.

1769. The monument to Spiritualists on Troup Street is a scaled-down model of what national statue?

1770. In 1977, WBBF disc jockey Hans Petersen released a comedy album entitled *Trust Me,* featuring Hans' impersonations. Who was the "star" of the LP?

1771. Locals drafted in this war were paid $12 when they signed up.

1772. It's the oldest college in Monroe County.

1773. This Rochester mayor from 1955-61 could trace his heritage to Rochester nursery pioneers, and served as director of safety for RG&E.

1774. Most of the construction of the Erie Canal is attributed to workers from this ethnic group.

1775. Rochesterian John Edland was the first to raise serious questions in the aftermath of the re-taking of the Attica prison in 1971. What was his occupation?

1776. Is the Rochester Police Department divided into wards, sections, precincts, or divisions?

1777. Who was the first president of FIGHT in 1964?

1778. According to the myth, she wanders along the lakeshore with two German shepherds, seeking revenge for her daughter's death by haunting men who bring women to park by the lake. What is she called?

1779. The brown trout, now so much a part of upstate waters, was introduced into the area by Seth Green. He stocked the waters by importing the fish from what European country?

1780. He wasn't Sam Patch, but Rochesterians in 1981 had a newsmaker all their own known as "The Leaper." What was his occupation?

1781. According to the 1980 census, which does the city have the most of: doctors, lawyers, firefighters, or policemen?

1782. Of the following, which are (were) native Rochesterians: George Eastman, Joe Altobelli, Joseph C. Wilson, and Nathaniel Rochester?

1783. In the 1920's, Rochester physician John Williams, Sr. pioneered the use of this technique in the treatment of a blood sugar problem.

1784. It's the official name of the new downtown YMCA.

1785. Who were Julian Orr, L. Joe Miller, Kermit Hill, and Seymour Sher?

1786. According to the 1980 census, Rochester was home to 653 refugees from what country?

1787. This turkey gained fame meandering through neighborhoods of Irondequoit in 1980.

1788. Miss Nellie McElroy became the first woman to wear this uniform in Rochester, and the tenth in the nation in 1913.

1789. This statue "protects" the Lamberton Conservatory. What is it a replica of?

1790. What was Councilman Charles Schiano's nickname, earned as the City Council's GOP minority of one?

1791. Decades before 1964, this man said the race problem was "America's most perplexing question," and that it could only be resolved through education.

1792. This 12 million dollar proposal would have dramatically changed the view of Main Street in 1979.

1793. How many ramp garages does the city operate?

1794. What is the term of office for a Monroe County Court judge?

1795. Eastridge High is found in what school district?

1796. Which came first: Monroe County or the city of Rochester?

1797. In 1983, Congressman Frank Horton presented 300, or nearly one a day.

1798. The campaign to save this included 4,350 coupons clipped from the newspaper and mailed to President Reagan.

1799. Before lilacs, Rochester was already gaining a reputation as "The Flower City" with its acres of these that bloomed each spring.

1800. How many buildings make up Monroe Community College? They're numbered.

1801. His original epitaph read, "Here lies ________________. Such is fame."

1802. He was the first black-endorsed candidate to run for countywide office.

1803. She was personally responsible for a great deal of what is now East Rochester: including a park, a golf course, and Concrest—perhaps the first mass-produced housing development.

1804. This Rochesterian left for Missouri where he ultimately became a Democratic United States Senator.

1805. Fred Eckert was originally considered for an ambassadorship to another country before Fiji. Name it.

PEOPLE & PLACES

1806. What was Midge Costanza's title here when she left the city to work for Jimmy Carter in 1976?

1807. Where was Matthew Clark consecrated to the office of bishop of Rochester?

1808. These adorn Mercury's helmet and feet.

1809. When the Price Hotel burned down in 1891, this replaced it—until it, too, burned in 1981.

1810. Founders expected that 100-200 would participate in five daily prayer services at their Brighton site. What religion?

1811. Is Mary Therese Friel a pro golfer, poet-in-residence at Nazareth College, or a former Miss USA?

1812. When Arabella Granger arrived on December 5, 1800, she was the first in Rochester.

1813. Architect James Johnson won an open competition for his design of this downtown city landmark erected in 1965.

1814. Dancer-turned-artist Clare Luce presented the Memorial Art Gallery with a self-portrait. But the portrait depicted her as a historical figure. Who?

1815. The main campus of the U of R can now be found along Wilson Boulevard. But in the 1920's it had another address. What street?

1816. This composer's grandfather constructed a downtown office building that still bears his name.

1817. The University of Rochester admitted its first one in 1900.

1818. Where is Bishop Fulton Sheen buried?

1819. This was to be constructed downtown, 18 feet above the ground at a cost of somewhere between $25-167 million.

1820. Which represents a larger percentage of Rochester's Jewish community: the Conservative or the Reformed?

1821. He invented the mail chute and also served as Rochester's mayor during the great Sibley's fire of 1904.

1822. What's the official name of the main Rochester Public Library downtown?

1823. For nearly two decades, he's called himself "The Lone Crusader," circling City Hall in his "Ratmobile," a van topped with a papier-mache rat. His name, please?

1824. It has the only public outdoor wading pool in downtown Rochester.

1825. Superintendent Laval Wilson came to Rochester from a city that grabbed headlines in the 60's for its active college community. What's the city?

1826. How long will the city pound keep a stray dog before it is destroyed?

1827. It's known as the Skating Institute of Rochester. What was this downtown rink formerly called?

1828. He acquired the *Democrat & Chronicle* while owning the *Times-Union* in 1928.

1829. The founder of the Genesee Brewery, Louis A. Wehle, once acquired land along the St. Lawrence to begin a museum honoring this "giant" of French history.

1830. There is a large sign atop the building that houses the Four Corners branch of Empire Savings. What does the sign read?

1831. Built in the 1940's it was named after the daughter of a LeRoy man who made $67 million marketing Jell-O. It was supposed to be named "Q Wing," since all expansion was listed alphabetically. What was it named instead?

1832. St. Patrick's Day, 1981, was a big day for Corrine Beach. Why?

1833. Before George Eastman committed suicide, he placed a wet towel over his chest. Why?

1834. George Eastman's suicide note read: "My work is done. Why wait?" But there was more. What else was written on the note?

PEOPLE & PLACES ANSWERS

1526. Susan B. Anthony
1527. Three
1528. Usually, one hour and fifteen minutes, but it is adjustable!
1529. Frank Gannett
1530. From her yard; grass, berries, bark, weeds, etc.
1531. Thirteen
1532. Jennifer and Michael
1533. Just one—#46 in Henrietta
1534. Fred Eckert
1535. Beer
1536. None was born in Rochester, despite stories to the contrary.
1537. Yes—one
1538. Gold, befitting the god of commerce
1539. New York's Grand Central Station
1540. Jimmy, the oldest living chimp in captivity!
1541. Fight Square
1542. Hillel School
1543. So the curious couldn't compare them to dates of first born!
1544. Take your road test
1545. Pet cemeteries
1546. Genesee Valley Park
1547. Rattlesnake Pete (Gruber)
1548. They all are except Gannett.
1549. Fourteen years
1550. She was a Quaker.
1551. City Hall
1552. Terry Diehl
1553. Brigham Young
1554. Female students from the closed St. Agnes High
1555. 7 a.m. and 6 p.m.
1556. Stop
1557. Commandments
1558. Malaria
1559. Louise Brooks
1560. Sol Linowitz
1561. Vietnam
1562. Scottish
1563. Salt; it was the largest sea water pool in the world!
1564. Automobile Club of Rochester
1565. The Star Theater at the Strasenberg Planetarium
1566. Traffic accidents
1567. Park Avenue Project
1568. Margaret Woodbury Strong

PEOPLE & PLACES ANSWERS

1569. "Landslide" Lyndon Johnson (1964, running as a Democrat and Liberal)
1570. George Eastman
1571. "The Star Bandit"
1572. Spanish-American
1573. "In God We Trust"
1574. Canadians
1575. The United Way
1576. Sam Patch
1577. Susan B. Anthony coins
1578. RIT's City Center
1579. Kenneth B. Keating
1580. *Essence of Rochester*
1581. The Space Frame
1582. All named after Rochester bishops; Mooney became a Cardinal after he left Rochester for Detroit.
1583. Six miles per hour
1584. Iola
1585. Green and yellow
1586. The Beach quintuplets
1587. Nathaniel Rochester
1588. Republicans favored temperance!
1589. City School Board
1590. Alexander, New York
1591. Red
1592. Walter Carnahan
1593. Mt. Hope Cemetery
1594. Ice
1595. Spiritualism
1596. Thomas Edison
1597. Millers
1598. Salvation Army coin kettles
1599. Toronto
1600. Col. Thomas Schaeffer
1601. Pigeons
1602. District attorney ($65,000; $8,000 more than the judge)
1603. Rochester Savings Bank (Franklin Street office)
1604. $19 million
1605. She was an Iranian student.
1606. African Methodist Episcopal
1607. "Walk-Don't Walk"
1608. American Lung Association
1609. Arcadia, Athena and Olympia
1610. It was the star that guided slaves north to Canada and freedom.
1611. Abe Lincoln
1612. A burning torch and a water fountain

PEOPLE & PLACES ANSWERS

1613. Frederick Douglass
1614. "Do It for Rochester"
1615. Gates residents; there was never a name developed by or for them.
1616. "Organized crime"
1617. Sacred Heart Cathedral; it was held there to symbolize an "ecumenical spirit."
1618. Busing
1619. Iroquois Indians
1620. Monroe County; the operator is the County Executive.
1621. Hojack Line
1622. Don Holleder
1623. Genesee Brewery
1624. Buffalo Bill Cody (one of them, son Kit Carson)
1625. Between 6 and 7 p.m.
1626. Frank Valenti
1627. Music; they all played in the 1817 Rochester Band.
1628. Abe Lincoln
1629. RTS Route #1
1630. There was supposed to be a working fountain springing up from the Genesee at the fork in the Y; it was clogged and never worked.
1631. Monroe County Airport
1632. Three cents
1633. East High—1903 (West—1904)
1634. Margaret
1635. One
1636. Bloomers (Amelia Bloomer)
1637. Moral Majority
1638. Gambling
1639. Ordained minister
1640. The dandelion
1641. Glenn Hammond Curtiss
1642. It was fireproof!
1643. Frederick Douglass
1644. Skyscraper
1645. Congresswoman Jessica "Judy" Weis
1646. State School at Industry
1647. "Jimmy the Hammer"
1648. Bernard Gifford
1649. Carrie Nation
1650. 705 elections inspectors are given 15¢ to phone in returns. The extra nickel because many ran out of time on their dime.
1651. In Highland Park
1652. Asphalt
1653. Baby Boom
1654. Stone-Tolan House

PEOPLE & PLACES ANSWERS

1655. Sam Patch
1656. Italian
1657. "All-American City"
1658. Temple Beth Shalom (5.5%)
1659. Brighton
1660. An insect that damaged the wheat crop
1661. The length of skirts
1662. National Technical Institute for the Deaf
1663. Robert F. Kennedy
1664. Home for Fallen Women
1665. Four
1666. 65 and over
1667. *Geo*
1668. Factions of the city's organized crime population
1669. Alfred and Androv
1670. *The Book of Mormon*
1671. Philharmonic conductor
1672. Board of Cooperative Educational Services
1673. Louis Pasteur
1674. Lawyer
1675. The Eastman Memorial on the Lake Avenue side of Kodak Park
1676. Max Farash
1677. Eastman Theatre
1678. Sixty feet
1679. Twelve
1680. Who should get the vote first; white women or black men
1681. Reverend Robert Spears
1682. All former presidents of FIGHT
1683. No parking
1684. St. Joseph's Church
1685. Quit school to go to work
1686. The wind blew it down.
1687. Rochester Museum and Science Center
1688. People who lived along them did it to earn credits against their property taxes.
1689. They've all been names for the same building on River Road. (Currently it's The Riverboat.)
1690. Washington Square
1691. Rebuilding each city road!
1692. Roberts Wesleyan College
1693. Cars
1694. German dairy farmers supplied most of the city's butter.
1695. 111
1696. Reynolds Arcade
1697. George Eastman
1698. *Fred and Ginger*

PEOPLE & PLACES ANSWERS

1699. Reformed Judaism
1700. It was cut from white marble.
1701. The Corinthian
1702. Frank Valenti
1703. Mt. Hope Cemetery (by nearly 100,000!)
1704. Durand-Eastman Park
1705. Gates
1706. Tonsils
1707. Times Square Building
1708. Salvation Army
1709. High-rise apartment complex
1710. Ken Keating (1958)
1711. Rochester's Public Library
1712. Former Rochesterians convicted for the Hillside Strangler murders
1713. Rene Piccarretto
1714. A mongrel dog named Idaho
1715. A hydrofoil boat
1716. Iroquois women participated in the selection of the chief.
1717. 1991; Samuel Dicker served 16 years; Ryan's term began in 1974.
1718. William (Bill) Smith
1719. "Little White House"
1720. Camp Haccamo
1721. Residential houses
1722. It began above ground; only at South Avenue did it go underneath buildings.
1723. University of Rochester
1724. The Underground Railroad
1725. They're all Rochester's Sister Cities.
1726. Jewish
1727. Red Jacket
1728. Frederick Douglass' real name
1729. Monroe County Jail
1730. Rochester School for the Deaf
1731. Automobile
1732. Contagious illness inside; ex. pink = measles
1733. Mt. Hope Cemetery
1734. Four Corners
1735. Shoes
1736. Frederick Douglass
1737. *Mount Allegro*
1738. Red Smith
1739. Hattie Harris
1740. 32.3% (nearly 1-in-3)
1741. George Eastman

PEOPLE & PLACES ANSWERS

1742. Dropping out
1743. Lollypop Farm
1744. Renovated city homes with brightly-colored trim
1745. Canaltown
1746. Two
1747. Sheriff William Lombard
1748. He was the son of Chinese Premier Deng Xiaoping.
1749. People with infectious diseases were quarantined there.
1750. Kodak bonus
1751. Female doctor
1752. The sight of flowing water would promote temperance; the statue was destroyed "mysteriously" in the night.
1753. Women members
1754. Santa Claus
1755. The aster, developed by nurseryman James Vick
1756. Col. Nathaniel Rochester
1757. "Red" Emma Goldman
1758. Voting machine
1759. "Boondoggle"
1760. Franklin Roosevelt
1761. He slept continuously!
1762. Indian god
1763. Flapping-wing flight
1764. George Eastman
1765. Public Safety Building, Monroe County Jail, Hall of Justice
1766. Polygamy
1767. Whose building would be taller
1768. William Randolph Hearst
1769. Washington Monument
1770. Jimmy Carter
1771. War of 1812
1772. SUNY at Brockport (Brockport Academy—1848)
1773. Peter Barry
1774. Irish
1775. Monroe County Medical Examiner
1776. Sections
1777. Minister Franklin Florence
1778. The White Lady
1779. Germany
1780. Bank robber; he knocked off 9 banks by jumping over tellers' counters.
1781. 603 police (585 firefighters, 554 lawyers, 440 doctors)
1782. Only one; Xerox founder Joseph C. Wilson
1783. Insulin injection
1784. Chester F. Carlson Metro Center YMCA
1785. All former Rochester city managers

1786. Vietnam
1787. Morris
1788. A policewoman's uniform
1789. A cannon
1790. Lonesome Charlie
1791. George Eastman
1792. Pedestrian mall
1793. Six
1794. 10 years
1795. East Irondequoit
1796. Monroe County—1821
1797. Flags flown over the Capitol
1798. Rochester Weather Bureau
1799. Tulips
1800. Ten
1801. Sam Patch
1802. Charles Willis, County Court judge—1979
1803. Kate Gleason
1804. Stuart Symington
1805. New Zealand
1806. Vice-mayor
1807. St. Peter's Basilica in Rome, Italy
1808. Wings
1809. The Rush Hotel
1810. Moslem
1811. Former Miss USA
1812. Baby girl to be born
1813. Liberty Pole
1814. Joan of Arc
1815. Prince Street
1816. Alec Wilder
1817. Female student
1818. St. Patrick's Cathedral, New York City
1819. A people mover
1820. Reformed 42% (Conservative and Orthodox make up the rest)
1821. James Cutler
1822. Rundel Memorial Library
1823. Roy Fries
1824. Manhattan Square Park
1825. Berkeley
1826. Five working days
1827. Boys' Club rink
1828. Frank Gannett
1829. Napoleon
1830. Columbia Banking
1831. R Wing (Helen Rivas)

PEOPLE & PLACES ANSWERS

1832. She gave birth to quintuplets.
1833. The sparks from the gunshot might ignite a fire that would destroy his house, so the theory goes.
1834. "To my friends" before the message, and the initials "G.E.," after.

Dear *Rochestrivians,*

We know it's virtually impossible to collect and condense all the *ROCHESTRIVIA* bubbling under this great city. This book is just the beginning!

If you know a good piece of *Rochestrivia,* or if your very life is walking testament to Rochestrivia, we'd like to know about it. Just rip out this page, fill out this form below and put it in an envelope and mail it to us.

There just might be a *SON OF ROCHESTRIVIA* and we'd love to list your question (with due credit given to you) as part of it!

Pete Dobrovitz

P.S. If you have a photo that applies to your question, include it too. We'll get it back to you.

Here's my ROCHESTRIVIA Question:

____

____

____

____

____

Answer:

____

____

Here's my source:

____

____

NAME: __________________________________

ADDRESS: ________________________________

____

Send to: Big Kids, PO Box 10237, Rochester 14610